ALISON M. JONES

NUTRITION AND COOKERY
FOR NURSERY NURSES

LONGMAN   London and New York

Longman Group UK Limited,
Longman House, Burnt Mill, Harlow,
Essex CM20 2JE, England
and Associated Companies throughout the world.

First published 1988

British Library Cataloguing in Publication Data
Jones, Alison M.
    Nutrition and cookery for nursery nurses.
    1. Children — Nutrition   2. Day care
centres
    I. Title
    613.2′088054   RJ206

ISBN 0-582-41385-0

Set in Linotron 202 10/12pt Times
Produced by Longman Group (FE) Limited
Printed in Hong Kong

CONTENTS

ACKNOWLEDGEMENTS

We are indebted to the following for permission to reproduce copyright material:

Crown Copyright for data in Tables 3.1, 3.2, 3.3, 6.1, 6.2 and 7.1, which has been adapted with permission of the Controller of Her Majesty's Stationery Office.

Author's acknowledgements

I wish to thank the following people who helped me in the preparation of this book:

Eric Evans for the food illustrations, Dee and Jill for typing and Alison and Colin for proof reading.

1

NUTRITION:
CHOOSING A HEALTHY DIET

INTRODUCTION

Food plays an important part in everyone's life. Not only is food vital for life but we use food to enjoy ourselves, we both 'eat to live' and 'live to eat'.

On special occasions, e.g. birthdays, weddings and Christmas, we may find ourselves overeating, but for the rest of the year we need to eat food in the correct balance. This should start from childhood as bad food habits developed at an early age are difficult to break.

Food provides us with substances that will:
- maintain life and promote growth and repair of body tissues;
- produce energy for warmth and movement;
- regulate body processes.

The substances in food that supply these functions are called *nutrients*. There are six main groups of nutrients: (1) protein; (2) fat; (3) carbohydrate; (4) vitamins; (5) minerals; (6) water.

Pure protein, fat and carbohydrate all provide *energy*; these are known as *macronutrients*. Vitamins and minerals do not provide energy; these are *micronutrients*. Water is a nutrient because it is vital for life.

The study of nutrients, the foods that contain them and the way in which our bodies make use of them is called *nutrition*.

Foods are very complex mixtures which usually contain many nutrients in different amounts. Some foods are good sources of some nutrients and poor sources of others. This is why we need to eat a variety of foods to get the right balance of nutrients.

The food that a person eats everyday is known as his *diet*. Everyone has a diet (assuming that everyone eats!) but some people follow special diets, e.g. slimming diets, low-salt diets.

If the diet a person eats each day contains adequate amounts of all the nutrients, it is *balanced*. Some people do not eat the right balance of foods and become *malnourished*. Many people are in poor health because they do not have enough to eat; they are *undernourished*. This is often caused through wars, poverty and natural disasters. Even in our affluent society people can be malnourished; not because they do not have enough to eat but because they eat too much or make the wrong choice of food. Many diseases of modern society can be caused by a faulty diet, e.g. obesity (overweight), dental decay and heart disease.

CHOOSING A HEALTHY DIET

Which foods should we eat and what should we encourage children to eat in order to stay healthy?

The food we eat should contain adequate amounts of all the nutrients. If we ate a diet of sweets, chocolate and 'pop' constantly our health would soon begin to suffer and we would feel weak and lethargic and prone to infection and disease. Eating a good diet does not necessarily mean that these foods should be excluded from the diet; nor does it mean that we should live on some foods which historically have been considered as 'nutritious', such as fatty red meat, cheese, butter and milk. The aim of a healthy diet is to get the 'balance' right so that we feel well, our weight remains constant (within the right range for height) and that we are not eating too much or too little of foods which may influence our health in the long term.

In the past nutritionists have considered a good diet in terms of foods required in order to prevent nutritional deficiencies. The majority of people in the UK today eat a diet that is fairly healthy in this respect, i.e. most nutritional deficiencies are unknown in the UK. However, after some considerable research and debate over the years, most health professionals including doctors and nutritionists are now agreeing that excessive or insufficient intake of some nutrients can lead to the development of many diseases prevalent in modern society, e.g. obesity, dental decay, heart disease and bowel disorders, and therefore a balanced diet takes on a new meaning. It is important that children should be encouraged to have a healthy diet right from the start to prevent such disorders later on in life.

Achieving a healthy diet does not involve calculating intakes of nutrients from food tables each day; food should be enjoyable and not involve a maths lesson every mealtime! A healthy diet can easily be achieved by thinking of food in terms of 'groups' and choosing food from within each group daily.

THE FIVE FOOD GROUPS

1 MEAT AND ALTERNATIVES

This includes:

Meat
: All types: beef, pork, ham, bacon, lamb, rabbit, chicken and turkey, liver and kidney.

Fish
: All types.

Cheese
: Hard cheese is high in fat so eat moderate amounts only, unless it is a reduced fat variety. Hard cheese also contains a lot of salt. Cottage and curd cheeses are lower in fat. Cream cheese is not an alternative to meat.

Eggs
: These are a good source of protein, but egg yolk is high in cholesterol.

Pulses
: These include peas, beans and lentils. They are cheap alternatives to meat.

Nuts
: These can be used as a meat alternative but do contain fat. Nuts should not be given to young children as they may choke on them.

Meat and meat alternatives (Fig. 1.1) provide protein, B vitamins and iron (mainly meat sources). Meat is an expensive source of protein; cheaper cuts of meat contain the same nutritional value, e.g. minced meat, stewing steak with the fat removed. Some cheap meats, e.g. liver and kidney, are excellent sources of protein, minerals and iron and contain little fat.

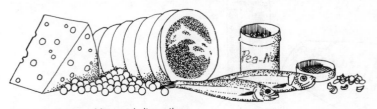

FIG. 1.1 Group 1: Meat and alternatives

2 DAIRY FOODS

Milk is nature's food and our only source of nourishment in the first 3–4 months of life. Children need more milk than adults; 1 pint per day for children and ½ pint for adults. Whole milk does contain a lot of fat and therefore it is healthier for adults to have a total or partial replacement of whole milk with semi-skimmed or skimmed milk, where the fat has been removed. Skimmed milk should not be given to children under 5 years as they need the energy provided by whole milk. Low fat yoghurt is a good alternative to milk, especially if a child does not like the taste of milk.

Cream contains a high proportion of fat and should be taken only occasionally.

Milk and dairy products (Fig. 1.2) provide protein, calcium and vitamins A and D. Children especially need calcium and vitamin D for the development of strong bones and teeth.

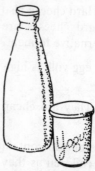

FIG. 1.2 Group 2: Dairy foods

3 BREAD, CEREALS AND POTATOES

This group supplies several important nutrients in the diet, e.g. carbohydrates, B vitamins. Bread and cereals provide protein,

FIG. 1.3 Group 3: Bread, cereals and potatoes

although of a low biological value. Potatoes are an important source of vitamin C. This group also helps to satisfy the appetite.

Bread, cereals and potatoes (Fig. 1.3) are all a valuable source of fibre in the diet. Wholemeal or white bread with added bran or vegetable fibre, wholegrain cereals, e.g. wholewheat pasta, brown rice or grainy breakfast cereals and potatoes baked or boiled in their skins are the best source of fibre in this group.

In recent years this group of food has suffered because the public thought that they were high in calories. The energy value of these foods is high if fat is added to them in large quantities, e.g. buttered bread, roast and chipped potatoes. On their own or with the addition of a little fat, these foods do not provide a great deal of energy and should be included in the diet because of their fibre content.

4 VEGETABLES AND FRUIT

Fruit and vegetables (including salads) are filling and provide vitamins, minerals and fibre (Fig. 1.4). Fruit, especially citrus fruit and blackcurrants, and green vegetables are important sources of vitamin C in the diet.

We should eat at least one item of fruit each day and two servings of vegetables. Fresh or frozen vegetables are preferable to canned vegetables as these contain salt and some of the vitamin C is lost in the canning process.

If children refuse fruit or vegetables pure unsweetened orange juice can be given as an alternative.

FIG. 1.4 Group 4: Vegetables and fruit

5 FATS AND OILS

This group (Fig. 1.5) provides a lot of energy and intake should be limited. Fried foods absorb some of the fat they are cooked in and so it is healthier to grill, boil or bake food.

Butter and margarine contain vitamins A and D. It is healthier to eat less fat altogether, particularly from animal sources such as butter, lard, dripping and suet.

A lot of the food we eat contains 'hidden' fat, e.g. in cakes, pastry, chocolate, salad dressings, processed meats. These foods should be eaten sparingly.

FIG. 1.5 Group 5: Fats and oils

FLUIDS

Water is essential for all body functions and it is important that everyone, especially children, has enough to drink each day.

However, it is important to remember that most fizzy drinks and squashes contain sugar; unsweetened fruit juices and water are preferable.

SUGAR

Sugar only contributes energy to the diet and causes overweight and dental decay, especially if a child develops a 'sweet tooth'.

It would be difficult and very boring to cut out sweets, chocolate, preserves, biscuits, cakes and puddings completely from the diet, but they should be eaten in small quantities only.

SALT

A high salt intake is dangerous for babies and young children because their kidneys have not matured sufficiently to excrete it. Later in life a high salt intake can cause high blood pressure so it is a good idea to use only a small amount in cooking and very little or none at the table. It is easy to develop a taste for less salty foods.

Like fat and sugar a lot of foods contain 'hidden' salt, e.g. processed meat, fish and vegetables, crisps, cheese, salted nuts and stock cubes.

In summary, in order to have a healthy diet we should aim to eat a selection of foods from the five food groups each day and also to eat:

- less meat but more meat alternatives;
- less dairy foods;
- more bread, cereals and potatoes;
- more fruit and vegetables;
- less fats and oil;
- less sugar;
- less salt.

QUESTIONS

1. Write down everything you have to eat for one day.
2. Is your diet healthy? How can you change it so that it is?
3. Write a day's menu following the above guidelines.

SPECIMEN ANSWER TO QUESTION 3

A healthy day's menu

Breakfast	Unsweetened orange juice Bowl of high fibre muesli with semi-skimmed milk
Snack	Banana
Lunch	Wholemeal bread filled with grated cheese and salad One slice of fruit cake One apple
Snack	Peanuts and raisins
Evening meal	Chilli con carne Brown rice Side salad Lemon sorbet
Bedtime	Wholemeal toast

2

NUTRITIONAL PROBLEMS OF MODERN SOCIETY

The food that most people in the UK eat is sufficiently well balanced to prevent nutritional deficiencies. But, as stated in Chapter 1, the food we eat does not create good health, since many diseases of our modern society can be caused wholly, or in part, by what we have eaten.

During the twentieth century our food has gradually altered; we consume more refined foods such as white bread and sugar, more fat and fatty foods, and more salt from processed foods. These changes have been paralleled by an increase in certain disorders, e.g. obesity, dental decay, heart disease and bowel disorders. The increase in consumption of processed foods has also led to an increase in the number of additives eaten, especially in the last 20–30 years.

Recent research has shown that a faulty diet in childhood can cause early changes which can lead to heart disease. Certainly bad teeth and overweight can be prevented by a good diet from the start of life.

OBESITY

Obesity is the most common nutritional disorder in the UK and other affluent countries. Recent surveys have shown that in adults, 39 per cent of men and 32 per cent of women are overweight. Obesity is not only found in adults; many children are fat and this can cause a great deal of unhappiness as well as being socially and medically undesirable.

People become overweight because their intake of energy is in excess of their requirement for energy, i.e. they eat more than they need so that the excess is stored as fat in adipose tissue. Many fat people do not eat any more than leaner people. It is just that their bodies may require less energy and the excess is laid down as fat. Overweight people tend to exercise less than thinner people; to lose weight permanently it is necessary to reduce the intake of energy and increase energy expenditure by increasing exercise.

Obesity is undesirable because:

- The skeleton is not designed to carry an extra load; overweight people often develop flat feet and arthritis of the knees and hips. Abdominal hernias and varicose veins also develop.
- Overweight people are more prone to heart disease, diabetes, gall stones, chest infections and skin infections.
- Obese people are often slow and ungainly and are more prone to accidents than thinner people. Extra body fat can cause complications during operations.

SLIMMING

Obesity is such a problem in the UK that there is a wealth of information, help, slimming aids and products available to try to assist people with their weight loss.

A lot of the information available relies on quick methods of weight loss; using very few foods or specially prepared formula drinks or meals. This is not the way to achieve a permanent weight loss; the only successful way to lose weight and to keep it off is to reduce the energy content of the diet by making the correct choice of foods and to increase exercise.

Most quick weight loss diets depend on losses of body water and protein, rather than body fat. Initially people on slimming diets lose a lot of weight because they lose water, later on a weight loss of 1 kg (1–2 lb) per week is desirable. For a very overweight person to reach target weight may take many months and it is during this time that will-power and determination are needed. After weight loss has been achieved it is very easy to increase weight if a permanent change in eating patterns has not been achieved. Slimming clubs are successful because meeting other slimmers is an encouragement to keep to a diet.

In order to lose weight it is necessary to reduce the amount of energy consumed and to keep the diet balanced (Fig. 2.1); this can be achieved by:

- cutting out sugar, sweets, chocolate, sweetened fizzy drinks and squashes, cakes, puddings, pies, biscuits, pastry, fried foods, cream, oil, fatty meat, cream cheese and alcohol;
- cutting down on red meat, cheese, bread, cereals, potatoes, butter and margarine;
- eating plenty of fruit and vegetables;
- using high-fibre varieties of bread and cereals to increase the bulk of the diet, using skimmed milk instead of whole milk, low-fat spreads instead of butter and margarine, low-calorie fizzy drinks and squashes.

FIG. 2.1 Low-energy foods

Slimming for children

Many children of fat parents also become fat due to either heredi-
tary or environmental factors (given too much to eat) or both. Many
fat children develop into fat adults with all the emotional and
medical factors associated with being overweight. Often an overweight child can be treated successfully by encouraging a healthy
choice of foods (see above), restricting sweets, sugar, sugary drinks
and crisps and cutting out fried foods. Often it is all the snacks eaten
that can cause children to put weight on; encourage plain biscuits
and fresh fruit if the child is very hungry. Usually, because of
growth, actual weight loss is not necessary; the child will grow and
therefore lose fat.

Anorexia nervosa

Anorexia nervosa is sometimes called the 'slimming disease'. It
occurs more frequently in adolescent girls and is due to excessive
slimming or an eating disorder where food is eaten in huge quantities followed by vomiting. The excessive weight loss can be life
threatening.

  Anorexia nervosa can be caused by several factors including
stress, e.g. of having school examinations, fear of growing up,
unhappiness about body weight and size. It can be controlled by
counselling and a more realistic food intake.

DENTAL CARIES

Dental decay or caries is such a common problem in the UK that
many people consider that having fillings is perfectly normal. Dental
decay usually comes to light during routine examinations at school
but usually begins much earlier in life and bad teeth are often found
in toddlers. About 30 per cent of all adults in England and Wales

have no natural teeth and it is still fairly uncommon to find anyone in a group of people with no filled teeth at all.

HOW DO DENTAL CARIES DEVELOP?

Dental caries develop when food, in particular sticky sugary foods, are deposited on teeth after eating. These deposits combine with saliva and bacteria normally present in the mouth to form a film called *plaque*. Plaque is almost invisible, but it can be shown by staining with a red dye. It forms mainly on the gum line, between the teeth and on the biting surfaces. Plaque can inflame the gums and if it is not removed it can become hard and contribute to *periodontal* or gum disease. Eventually the tooth will become loose and may fall out or need extracting. Periodontal disease also causes bleeding gums and bad breath.

The bacteria in the plaque will change sugars in foods to acids which dissolve the enamel coating on teeth. The enamel protects teeth so that when part is dissolved the rest of the tooth will start to decay. When the decay reaches the dentine hot and cold food may cause pain. Dentine is softer than enamel and decay can spread rapidly. If the decay reaches the soft pulp the nerve of the tooth is affected. This can be very painful. If not repaired or extracted by this stage an abscess can form, causing acute pain (see Fig. 2.2).

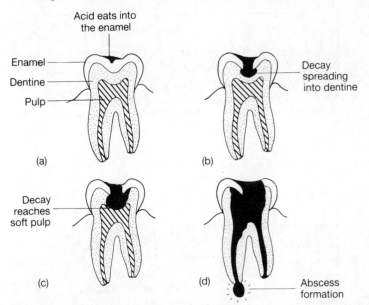

FIG. 2.2 Stages in dental decay: (a) start of tooth decay; (b) decay may be painful especially with hot and cold foods; (c) nerve fibres are affected by this stage – very painful; (d) abscesses may form from infection. Acute pain can lead to removal of the tooth

PREVENTION OF DENTAL DECAY

Every time we eat something sugary or have a sweet drink we are increasing the acidity of the mouth which can cause the enamel to dissolve and cause caries.

The two graphs in Fig. 2.3 show the effect of: (1) confining sweet foods to mealtimes only, and (2) eating and drinking sweet foods constantly throughout the day. In the second case the conditions for decay are increased considerably, as shown by the graph falling into the shaded region.

The acidity of the mouth can therefore be reduced by confining sugar consumption to mealtimes only; this particularly applies to children who should not be given sweets, biscuits and fizzy drinks constantly throughout the day, as this encourages a liking for sweet foods as well as being harmful to the teeth and causing weight gain.

It is also important not to give babies 'comforters', e.g. sweet syrups, or to add sugar or honey on to dummies as this can lead to severe caries developing on the incisors as well as encouraging a sweet tooth.

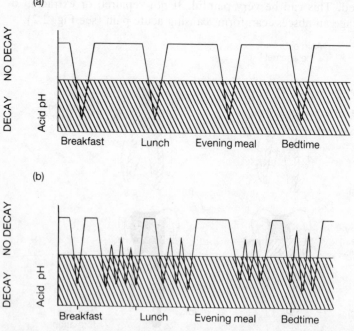

FIG. 2.3 (a) Confining consumption of sweet foods to mealtimes; (b) eating and drinking sweet foods throughout the day

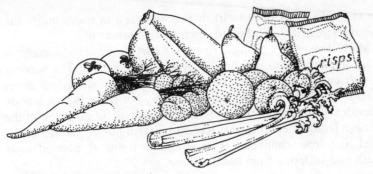

FIG. 2.4 Fruit and savoury snacks

Sugar in tea and coffee is just as harmful as sugar in food; try and gradually cut down on the amount of sugar added to drinks; it is possible to become accustomed to the taste of tea and coffee without sugar; you will probably then find sweetened drinks dreadful! Children can take weak tea and coffee without sugar – it is far better never to add it to their drinks in the first place. It is better to give savoury snacks to children, e.g. crisps, celery, carrot or fruit (see Fig. 2.4).

Correct cleaning of teeth is also essential in preventing decay. There is no point in cleaning teeth twice a day if they are brushed incorrectly. Many leaflets from dentists explain the correct technique. A dental hygienist will also give instruction.

In parts of the country where fluoride is present in the water supply the incidence of caries is lower; the addition of fluoride to the water supplies and in toothpastes can help prevent caries by strengthening the enamel to make it more resistant to acid attack. Fluoridation of water and toothpaste helps to prevent decay in children and adults. Only 10 per cent of water supplies with low levels of fluoride have it added as many people object to having their water supplies interfered with.

Dental caries and periodontal disease can be prevented by:
- Regular and correct cleaning of teeth.
- Reduced consumption of sweet sticky foods and drinks, especially as in-between meal snacks and as comforters to young children.
- Regular visits to the dentist.

HEART DISEASE

The UK death rates from coronary heart disease are among the highest in the world. It is the major cause of death and in 1980 31 per cent of deaths from heart disease occurred in males under the age of 65 years. Heart disease, therefore, shortens life.

Many factors are thought to play a part in the development of heart disease, one of which is the type of food we eat. The nutrient or nutrients causing heart disease have been the subject of many years of medical research and controversy but there is now a body of evidence suggesting that the amount and type of fat eaten in the diet can lead to heart disease. Recent research has also shown that a good diet from childhood is important in trying to prevent early death and suffering from heart disease.

THE DEVELOPMENT OF HEART DISEASE

Heart disease develops when the linings of the arteries (vessels carrying blood from the heart) become 'furred' up with fatty deposits so that blood cannot flow freely.

If the arteries nearest the heart, the cardiac arteries, become blocked or narrowed, blood supply to the heart can fail, causing a heart attack or myocardial infarction. The patient has severe pain in the chest which often radiates down the left arm. This can cause sudden death, or if the person recovers, there is an increased risk of having a second attack.

Often people have warnings that they have heart disease; angina pectoris is severe chest pain caused by exercise or excitement. Many drugs help control the pain; people with angina have an increased risk of having a heart attack.

RISK FACTORS

Studies have shown that the following factors may increase the risk or likelihood of developing heart disease:
• lack of exercise;
• smoking;
• stress;
• a family history of coronary heart disease;
• obesity;
• high blood pressure (hypertension);
• high fat and cholesterol levels in the blood.

No one factor will cause coronary heart disease; it is a combination of all or some of these factors.

Coronary heart disease can be prevented by trying to avoid all the risk factors mentioned above. It is impossible to alter one's family history but certainly we can make sure we take regular exercise; not just when at school but throughout our life; we should try and keep calm and not become too stressed (easier said than done!). If you smoke you should try to give it up. You should certainly not start smoking. If you are overweight you should try and reach your ideal weight.

Hypertension and raised fat and cholesterol levels in the blood can be prevented by two dietary measures:

1. Reduction in salt intakes to reduce blood pressure.
2. Reduction in the total fat consumed, particularly saturated fats.

Saturated fats (see Ch. 3) are mainly from animal sources, e.g. butter, lard, cream, dripping, cheese, milk and fatty meat, and may lead to an increase in the amount of cholesterol in the blood. Cholesterol is found in the fatty deposits causing narrowing of the arteries.

DISORDERS OF THE LARGE INTESTINE

Constipation, diverticular disease and other bowel disorders which are common in the UK and other developed countries are unknown in less developed parts of the world. Research has shown that the diet of people in the Third World contain a high proportion of dietary fibre, something which the diet in twentieth-century Britain lacks.

Fibre is important in digestion because it aids the movement of waste products down the large intestine. Dietary fibre is not digested; it is important because it holds water, thus making the faeces bulky, soft and easy to pass out of the body.

Constipation occurs because the faeces are very hard and small so that they only move slowly down the intestines. A lot of effort is needed to expel them, often causing bursting of small blood vessels around the anus or haemorrhoids which bleed. Because a lot of effort is needed to expel hard and small faeces, pressure can build up in the large intestine. The increase in pressure can cause the muscular walls to develop blown-out pouches to help lower the pressure. These pouches are known as *diverticula* and the person is said to have diverticular disease (see Fig. 2.5). If the pouches become inflamed severe pain can result; this can be partially relieved by a high-fibre diet.

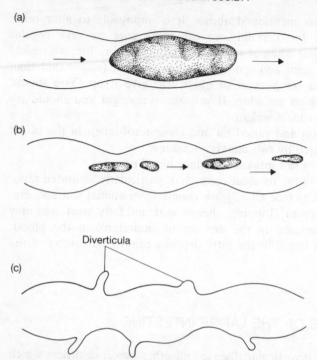

FIG. 2.5 (a) With a high-fibre diet large soft faeces move easily along the intestine; (b) if the diet lacks fibre small hard faeces form which require a lot of pressure to move them down the large intestine; (c) to help to relieve the pressure the walls of the large intestine herniate and form diverticula

FOOD ADDITIVES

Food additives are natural or artificially produced chemicals which are added to processed foods in very small amounts. In the last 20–30 years the consumption of processed foods in the UK has increased dramatically, and this has led to an increasing consumption of food additives. This is cause for concern because some people, especially children, can be allergic to particular additives. Although all additives undergo rigorous safety testing before being permitted for use little is known of any harmful effects of eating mixtures of these substances.

The shift towards healthier food with less fat, sugar and salt in processed foods has also led manufacturers to question the number of additives used, particularly colours. Many processed foods are now completely free from artificial colours and preservatives. Baby-food manufacturers observe a voluntary ban on the use of artificial colourings in baby foods sold in the UK.

To help the consumer identify food additives, the EEC have introduced a coding system for all additives throughout EEC countries. These are the 'E' numbers and are standard throughout the EEC. Since July 1986 Government legislation has required manufacturers to give more information on labelling of food additives on their products. All additives, artificial or natural, will have an 'E' code and this does not imply that they are harmful.

Additives labelled between E100 and E180 are colouring agents, E200 to E283 are preservatives. E300 to E321 are antioxidants (substances that prevent fatty foods such as butter going rancid). Additives coded E322 to E572 are stabilising agents and thickeners used in processed foods. Additives that do not have an 'E' number have to be written in full on food labels.

A small number of children can be allergic to certain colours in foods causing hyperactivity or asthma and eczema. These conditions are diagnosed medically and the appropriate diet is explained by a qualified dietitian.

QUESTIONS

1. Plan a day's menu for a slimmer which is balanced but does not contain high-energy foods.
2. Describe what happens when acid attacks a tooth.
3. List five foods which you could give to a child to eat as a snack which are not harmful to the teeth.
4. What are the factors which may make people more likely to suffer from coronary heart disease?
5. Explain why diverticular disease develops.

SPECIMEN ANSWER TO QUESTION 1

A day's menu for a slimmer

Breakfast   100 ml unsweetened orange juice
                 1 boiled egg
                 1 slice wholemeal toast

Lunch   100 g cottage cheese
                 Salad
                 2 crispbread biscuits
                 1 pear

Evening meal	75 g roast chicken
	75 g baked potato
	Green beans and carrots
	1 apple chopped in 50 ml natural yoghurt
Bedtime	1 crispbread
Over the day	250 ml skimmed milk
	15 g butter or margarine

3

THE VALUE OF FOOD: ENERGY AND MACRONUTRIENTS

ENERGY

The energy value of food is measured in *kilocalories* (normally abbreviated to kcal) (or Calories) or in the SI units *kilojoules* (normally abbreviated to kJ). There are 4.2 kJ to 1 kcal.

The energy in foods is contained within protein, fat, carbohydrate and alcohol:

1 g of pure protein yields 17 kJ (4 kcal)
1 g of pure carbohydrate yields 17 kJ (4 kcal)
1 g of pure fat yields 37 kJ (9 kcal)
1 g of pure alcohol yields 29 kJ (7 kcal)

As fat contains more than twice the energy as protein or carbohydrate, any foods containing a lot of fat are high-calorie foods.

Water does not provide any energy so foods with a high water content and little fat will contain very few calories, e.g. fruit and vegetables.

Table 3.1 shows the energy value of some common foodstuffs, in average portion sizes.

WHY DO WE NEED ENERGY?

We need energy for the following:
- muscle action;
- basal metabolism: this is the amount of energy required for the organs of the body to function, e.g. keeping the heart beating, keeping blood oxygenated and maintaining body temperature.

So even when we are not using muscles at all, we are still using energy in order to stay alive.

HOW MUCH ENERGY DO WE NEED?

Our requirements for energy are variable. People doing heavy physical work need more energy than office workers. Women tend to need less energy than men, except during pregnancy and lactation

TABLE 3.1 The energy value of some foodstuffs

Food and quantity	Kilocalories	Kilojoules
Biscuits		
Custard cream (1)	51	215
Milk chocolate digestive (1)	74	310
Rich tea (1)	45	192
Bread		
White bread (1 thin slice)	70	297
Wholemeal bread (1 thin slice)	65	275
Cakes		
Dundee (50 g)	165	700
Fancy gateau (50 g)	208	859
Cereals		
Cornflakes (15 g)	55	235
Muesli (15 g)	55	235
Weetabix (1)	85	361
Flour (15 g)	52	224
Rice (raw, 15 g)	90	384
Spaghetti (raw, 15 g)	95	403
Eggs		
Raw or boiled (1)	80	337
Fried (1)	128	529
Fats and oils		
Butter (15 g)	110	450
Margarine (15 g)	110	450
Fish		
Cod (baked, 100 g)	96	408
Cod in batter (fried, 100 g)	200	840
Kippers (100 g)	205	855
Salmon (tinned, 50 g)	78	325
Fruit		
Apple (125 g)	44	189
Banana (150 g)	70	303
Orange (125 g)	33	170
Meat		
Bacon (grilled, 1 rasher)	70	300
Beef (roast sirloin, 100 g)	284	1182
Chicken (roast, 100 g)	142	599
Lamb (chop, 150 g)	333	1392
Pork (chop, 150 g)	340	1418
Milk and milk products		
Whole milk (200 ml)	130	544
Skimmed milk (200 ml)	66	284
Cream (single, 15 g)	32	131
Cheddar cheese (25 g)	102	420
Cottage cheese (50 g)	48	201

Food and quantity	Kilocalories	Kilojoules
Yoghurt (natural, 150 ml)	78	324
Yoghurt (fruit, 150 ml)	143	608
Sugar and sugar products		
Sugar (25 g)	99	420
Marmalade (25 g)	65	279
Chocolate (milk, 25 g)	132	553
Clear fruits (25 g)	82	349
Toffees (25 g)	108	453
Vegetables		
Cabbage (boiled, 50 g)	5	20
Carrots (boiled, 50 g)	10	40
Cauliflower (boiled, 50 g)	5	20
Potatoes (boiled, 100 g)	80	343
Potatoes (chipped, 100 g)	253	1065
Tomatoes (50 g)	7	30

Source: McCance and Widdowson's 'The Composition of Foods' A. A. Paul and D. A. T. Southgate London, HMSO, 1978.

(milk production). We need extra energy when we are growing, so children and teenagers especially need a lot of food.

Table 3.2 shows the recommended daily amounts of energy required by some groups of the population. These figures are only a guide; many people find they may require more or less than the stated amount.

If the amount of energy consumed is greater than output, the excess will be converted to fat and stored as adipose tissue, causing weight gain.

TABLE 3.2 Recommended daily energy intakes

	Energy	
	Kilocalories	*Megajoules*
Children, age 1–2	1100–1400	4.5–5.75
Children, age 3–4	1500–1560	6.25–6.5
Children, age 5–6	1680–1740	7.0–7.25
Children, age 7–8	1900–1980	8.0–8.25
Teenagers	2150–2800	9.0–11.0
Women, age 18–54 (sedentary)	2150	9.0
Men, age 18–35 (sedentary)	2510	10.5

Source: *Recommended Daily Amounts of Food Energy and Nutrients for Groups of People in the United Kingdom*, London, HMSO, 1979.

MACRONUTRIENTS

PROTEIN

Functions

The human body is composed of millions of cells which contain protein. Each cell is replaced at certain intervals; so we need protein for replacement and also to repair any damaged cells. During childhood and adolescence new cells are laid down as the body grows, then extra protein is required.

Protein must be provided in the diet for growth and repair, but any extra protein that is eaten can be used to provide energy.

Composition

There are many different types of protein but all are composed of four elements: (1) oxygen; (2) carbon; (3) hydrogen; (4) nitrogen, and usually sulphur and phosphorus.

Proteins contain chains of smaller units called *amino acids*. A protein can consist of hundreds or even thousands of amino acids. There are about twenty-two different amino acids which are arranged in different combinations and quantities in the protein chains. It is the unique arrangement of amino acids which gives each protein its characteristic structure and properties.

In nutrition amino acids are very important. Because we are unable to synthesise or manufacture a certain number of them which are required for the growth and repair of cells, we need them in our diet. The amino acids which cannot be synthesised by the body are called the *essential amino acids*. In adults there are eight essential amino acids and in children there are ten.

Sources

Proteins that supply **all** the essential amino acids in sufficient quantities have a *high biological value* (HBV) and are mainly from animal sources (see Fig. 3.1):

- meat;
- fish;
- cheese;
- eggs;
- milk.

Proteins that lack one or more of the essential amino acids have a *low biological value* (LBV) and are usually plant foods (see Fig. 3.2):

FIG. 3.1 High biological value protein foods

FIG. 3.2 Low biological value protein foods

- cereals: wheat, rice, maize and their products, including bread;
- pulses: peas, beans and lentils;
- nuts.

Gelatine, made from animal bones, has a low biological value.

Usually different plant foods are low in different amino acids, so that if two plant protein foods are eaten together they can form a protein of high biological value; this is known as *complementation*, because each plant protein is complementing each other, e.g. beans on toast.

Textured vegetable protein (TVP) is made from soya beans which have been shaped, coloured and flavoured to resemble meat. The amino acid methionine which is low in soya beans is added, as well as other nutrients, so that TVP is also nutritionally comparable to meat.

Requirements

Everyone needs to eat protein to replace and repair body tissues but during periods of growth extra protein is required.

Children and adolescents need extra protein for growth. Pregnant women need extra protein for the growing baby and also when breast-feeding for milk production.

The recommended daily amount of protein for various groups are shown in Table 3.3. The figures are based on recommended amounts of energy so the recommended intakes vary for men and women.

TABLE 3.3 Recommended daily protein requirements

	Protein (g)
Children, age 1–2	27–35
Children, age 3–4	37–39
Children, age 5–6	42–43
Children, age 7–8	47–49
Teenagers	53–72
Women, age 18–54 (sedentary)	54
Men, age 18–35 (sedentary)	63

Source: *Recommended Daily Amounts of Food Energy and Nutrients for Groups of People in the United Kingdom*, London, HMSO, 1979.

Deficiency

In the UK we eat more than enough protein and so it is very rare to be deficient. However, it is more common in countries where there is insufficient food. This particularly affects children because their protein needs are very high. A deficiency of protein is usually associated with a total lack of food and can cause the following conditions:

• Marasmus: affecting mainly babies under 1 year. The body adapts to lack of food by muscle wasting and using fat stores in order to keep the vital organs functioning, e.g. heart, lungs, brain.
• Kwashiorkor: this affects older children and is poor adaptation to famine leading to retarded growth, diarrhoea, infections and fluid retention causing swelling.

Both these conditions will lead to death.

CARBOHYDRATES

Functions

Carbohydrates provide the body with energy. Starchy carbohydrates also provide the body with other nutrients and dietary fibre.

Composition

All carbohydrates are composed of carbon, hydrogen and oxygen and can be divided into three main groups: (1) monosaccharides; (2) disaccharides; (3) polysaccharides.

Monosaccharides

These simple sugars are the units from which more complicated carbohydrates are made. There are three important monosaccharides in nutrition. These are:

Glucose: is the form of carbohydrate found in the body as a source of energy. All carbohydrate is digested to glucose. Any protein that is not required for growth and repair can be converted to glucose and used as a source of energy. Glucose is a very concentrated source of energy and is often taken by athletes in a powdered or tablet form. It is also found in fruit and vegetables.

Fructose: or fruit sugar is found in fruit, vegetables and honey. It is the sweetest sugar known.

Galactose: is found only as part of lactose or 'milk sugar'.

Disaccharides

These consist of two monosaccharide sugars joined together.

Sucrose is ordinary sugar and is obtained from refining sugar cane and sugar beet. It is formed from one unit of glucose and one unit of fructose (see Fig. 3.3).

G	+	F	→	G – F
Glucose		Fructose		Sucrose

FIG. 3.3

Lactose is found in milk and is formed from one unit of glucose and one unit of galactose.

Maltose is formed during starch digestion and also during germination of cereals, e.g. barley. It is formed from two glucose units joining together.

Polysaccharides

Starches and fibre are complex forms of carbohydrate and are called polysaccharides.

Starch is formed from many glucose units joined together to form straight branched chains. Starch is a food reserve in root vegetables, cereals and pulses. In the raw state the starch granules are insoluble in water and so are difficult to digest, but on cooking in water the starch granules swell and become more easily digested.

Dietary fibre is a term covering several types of polysaccharides and related materials. These are usually found in plant cell walls and provide a rigid and fibrous structure of stems, leaves and husks of seeds.

Cellulose is a polysaccharide composed of glucose units. The glucose is of a slightly different structure from starch which makes it indigestible.

Pectin is a complex polysaccharide found in fruits and roots. It forms a stiff jelly which is used in jam making.

Dietary fibre also comprises hemicelluloses which are a group of polysaccharides. The constituents of dietary fibre are not nutrients because they cannot be digested by the human body but they are important as they add bulk to the diet and help in the correct functioning of the large bowel. The average UK diet is lacking in fibre which has caused many bowel disorders. We should therefore eat more foods containing fibre (see Ch. 1).

Sources of sugars

Sugars can be found in all types of table-top sugar (e.g. brown, granulated, icing), jams, marmalades, honey, sweets, chocolate, sweetened squashes, carbonated drinks, fruit and baked items made with sugar, e.g. cakes, biscuits, puddings (see Fig. 3.4).

Sugar and foods made almost entirely from sucrose such as sweets and sugary drinks provide us only with 'empty calories' – they provide only energy and no other nutrients. Excessive consumption of sugar can cause dental decay and obesity (see Ch. 2). Sugar is not essential to the diet. There is no real difference between brown and white sugar and honey.

Sources of starches and fibre

Starches can be found in bread, potatoes, breakfast cereals, rice, sweet corn, pasta (spaghetti, macaroni, etc.), pulses, flour and flour products, e.g. biscuits, cakes and pastry (see Fig. 3.5).

Starchy foods are useful because they are good sources of energy and other nutrients, e.g. protein, B vitamins. They are filling and relatively cheap to buy.

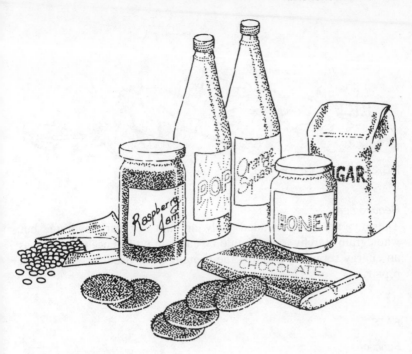

FIG. 3.4 Sources of sugar

FIG. 3.5 Sources of starch

Fibre is found in fruits, vegetables, especially those lightly cooked and jacket potatoes, wholegrain cereals, e.g. bran, wholemeal bread, brown rice, wholewheat pasta, wholewheat breakfast cereals (see Fig. 3.6).

FIG. 3.6 Sources of dietary fibre

Requirement

There is no recommended daily amount for carbohydrate, but wholegrain starchy foods should be eaten in preference to protein as an energy supplier, to allow the protein to be used for growth and repair.

FATS

Functions

The main function of fats is to provide the body with a concentrated form of energy. Fats will provide 9 kcal (37 kJ) per 1 g which is more than double the amount of energy supplied by pure protein and carbohydrate. Some fats also contain the fat-soluble vitamins, A, D, E and K.

Fatty foods are often digested very slowly and so provide a feeling of fullness for a long time after a meal – this is called a 'high satiety value'. Fats also add to the flavour and palatability of a meal. In the body fat covers some vital organs to protect them, e.g. glands and kidneys, and it also forms an insulating layer beneath the skin to help maintain body temperature. However, if we eat too much fat *obesity* (overweight) will result. Too much fat or certain types of fat may cause heart disease and so it is recommended that our intake of fat is reduced by about 30 per cent.

Composition

Like carbohydrates, fats contain carbon, hydrogen and oxygen. Fats consist of mixtures of *triglycerides*. Triglycerides are formed from two substances – glycerol and fatty acids. Only one glycerol unit joins with three fatty acid units to form a triglyceride (see Fig. 3.7).

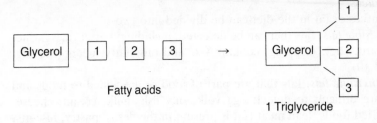

FIG. 3.7

In nutrition it is the fatty acids that are important. There are dozens of different fatty acids found in nature. They can either be saturated or unsaturated. This refers to the number of hydrogen atoms present in relation to the carbon atoms. The carbon atoms in fatty acids that are saturated cannot accept any more hydrogen atoms (see Fig. 3.8). But in an unsaturated fatty acid some of the carbon atoms are joined by a double bond and so could accept more hydrogen atoms (See Fig. 3.9). *Polyunsaturated* fatty acids contain more than one double bond.

Saturated fats are generally solid at room temperature and are generally from animal sources. Unsaturated fats are generally liquid at room temperature and are called oils. They are generally obtained from vegetable sources, with the exception of fish oils.

Cholesterol is a type of fat which is found in association with animal fats. It is also found naturally in the blood; very high levels can cause hardening of the arteries which can lead to heart disease. Polyunsaturated fats may lower blood cholesterol levels.

$$
\begin{array}{ccccc}
H & & H & & H \\
| & & | & & | \\
\cdots \quad C & - & C & - & C \quad \cdots \\
| & & | & & | \\
H & & H & & H
\end{array}
$$

FIG. 3.8 A saturated fat

$$
\begin{array}{ccccccccc}
H & & H & & H & & & & H \\
| & & | & & | & & & & | \\
\cdots \quad C & - & C & - & C & = & C & - & C \quad \cdots \\
| & & | & & & & | & & | \\
H & & H & & & & H & & H
\end{array}
$$

FIG. 3.9 An unsaturated fat

Sources

Sources of fat in the diet can be divided into two:

- *visible fats*: fats that can be detected, including: butter, margarine, lard, suet, dripping, cooking fats and oils, fatty meats (see Fig. 3.10).
- *Invisible fats*: fats that are part of food or are added to foods and are difficult to detect: egg yolk, oily fish, milk, cream, cheese, fried foods, lean meat (fat is present in the flesh), pastry, biscuits, cakes, chocolate (see Fig. 3.11).

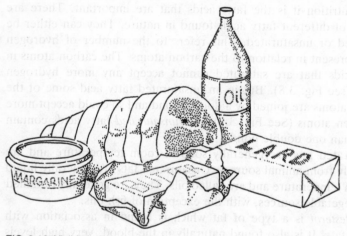

FIG. 3.10 Visible fats

FIG. 3.11 Foods containing 'invisible' fat

Requirements
Some fatty acids cannot be synthesised by the body and are essential. It is therefore necessary to eat small amounts of fat each day to provide the body with the essential fatty acids. In general, however, we eat far too much fat, especially animal fat. We would be healthier if we reduced the amount of fat eaten each day. This can be achieved by cutting down on fried foods, cream, cheese, fatty meat and using only a scraping of butter or margarine on bread.

WATER

About 70 per cent of the human body is water; it is essential for life. It is needed for most of the body processes; it transports materials around the body and also removes waste products. The balance of water retained in the body is carefully controlled by the kidneys.

Sources
Water comes from solid foods as well as from drinks. Some foods, e.g. fruit and vegetables, are mainly water.

Requirements
We need to drink at least 1500 ml (3½ pt) of water per day. Extra water is required during illness when the temperature is raised; also to replace losses following diarrhoea and vomiting.

QUESTIONS

1. List the six main groups of nutrients.
2. Why do we need energy?
3. Why are amino acids important in nutrition?
4. List three groups of people who require extra protein and explain why they do.
5. Why may sugars be harmful to the body?
6. List the sources of dietary fibre.
7. What is the difference between saturated and unsaturated fatty acids?
8. How can we reduce our fat intake?

MICRONUTRIENTS:
VITAMINS AND MINERALS

VITAMINS

Vitamins are required by the body in only very small quantities, but they are essential to the body because without them certain *deficiency diseases* can develop. In this country we have a varied diet with adequate supplies of all the vitamins and so real deficiences are rare. However, some groups with extra needs like children and pregnant women may be 'at risk' of developing deficiences if their diet is inadequate.

Most vitamins have been identified this century and can be divided into two groups:
• water-soluble vitamins: B group, vitamin C;
• fat-soluble vitamins: vitamins A, D, E and K.
It is important to eat foods containing adequate amounts of the water-soluble vitamins each day as these are not stored by the body. They are also easily lost during storage, preparation and cooking. Fat-soluble vitamins are stored in the body. If massive amounts of these vitamins are taken they may become toxic (poisonous) to the body.

WATER-SOLUBLE VITAMINS

B GROUP VITAMINS

There are at least thirteen different vitamins in this group, the majority of which are found in most foods and so a deficiency is rare. There are five important vitamins in this group, which can be divided into two categories, according to their function:
1. Those involved in the release of energy from food: thiamin (vitamin B_1); riboflavin (vitamin B_2), and nicotinic acid (vitamin B_3).
2. Those involved with cell division especially in the bone marrow which forms blood: folic acid and vitamin B_{12}.

Thiamin

Thiamin is necessary for the release of energy from carbohydrate foods.

Sources

Bread and flour, meat, especially pork, potatoes, milk, yeast extract, wholegrain cereals, especially wheatgerm and fortified breakfast cereals (see Fig. 4.1).

Thiamin is easily destroyed by high temperatures.

FIG. 4.1 Sources of thiamin

Requirement

The requirement for thiamin is linked to the amount of carbohydrate in the diet. As carbohydrate usually contributes up to 50 per cent of the total energy content of the diet, requirements of thiamin can be related to the amount of energy in the diet. The recommended daily amount is based on supplying 0.4 mg thiamin/1000 kcal.

Deficiency

A severe deficiency of thiamin leads to the disease *beriberi*. The symptoms are exhaustion, weight loss and muscle wasting. In one type of beriberi fluid may be retained in the body causing swelling.

Beriberi is rare in the UK but can occur where polished rice is a staple part of the diet. Mild symptoms of beriberi can occur if a diet rich in carbohydrate is taken without thiamin, e.g. in alcoholics.

Symptoms include depression, lack of memory, irritability, inflamed and painful nerves.

Riboflavin
Riboflavin is required for the release of energy from food.

Sources
Milk – this supplies about one-third of our daily requirement – meat, especially liver and eggs (see Fig. 4.2).

Riboflavin is easily destroyed by ultraviolet light (sunlight) and so milk should not be left out on the doorstep for long periods.

FIG. 4.2 Sources of riboflavin

Requirement
Riboflavin requirement is related to energy requirements at rest. The recommended amount is 1 mg/1000 kcal of resting metabolism.

Deficiency
There is no real deficiency disease associated with a lack of riboflavin. Cracks in the corners of the mouth and the tongue may become magenta colour if the diet is deficient.

Nicotinic acid
Nicotinic acid is also involved in the utilisation of energy from food.

Sources
Meat and meat products, bread and flour, fortified breakfast cereals, vegetables, milk and eggs (see Fig. 4.3).

Fruit and eggs contain only small amounts of nicotinic acid but

FIG. 4.3 Sources of nicotinic acid

they can provide this vitamin because they contain large quantities of the amino acid *tryptophan* which can be converted to nicotinic acid by the body.

Maize contains large quantities of nicotinic acid but this is unavailable to the body. In Mexico, however, maize is treated with limewater in the preparation of tortillas and this releases the nicotinic acid.

Requirement
The recommended daily amount for nicotinic acid is based on the amount needed for basal metabolism – 11.3 mg/1000 kcal. (see p. 19).

Deficiency
A lack of nicotinic acid in the diet leads to the disease *pellagra*. The symptoms are dermatitis, especially around the neck, dementia and diarrhoea. This is only a problem in areas of the world where maize is the staple (except the Mexican diet).

Folic acid and vitamin B_{12}
Folic acid and vitamin B_{12} are involved with cell division, especially rapidly dividing cells such as those in the bone marrow which form blood.

Sources
Folic acid is mainly found in fresh dark-green vegetables, liver and kidney. Cereals and pulses also contain a little folic acid. Folic acid

is readily destroyed by cooking, so care must be taken when cooking vegetables, in particular. (see Fig. 4.4).

Vitamin B_{12} is found exclusively in animal foods. Liver is the richest source (see Fig. 4.5). It is very difficult to become deficient in B_{12} except for strict vegans, but it is synthesised by bacteria in the gut. Vegans appear to be able to obtain sufficient B_{12} by this process. Vegans are vegetarians who do not eat any animal products. (see p. 71).

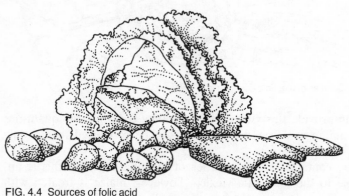

FIG. 4.4 Sources of folic acid

FIG. 4.5 Sources of vitamin B_{12}

Deficiency

Lack of folic acid in the diet causes a type of anaemia known as megaloblastic anaemia. The red blood cells that are formed in the bone marrow are abnormal and enlarged. This leads to the symptoms of anaemia – listlessness, fatigue, pale complexion.

To absorb vitamin B_{12} the body needs a special factor present in the stomach wall known as intrinsic factor. Sometimes this is missing and causes pernicious anaemia. This is corrected by monthly injections of B_{12}.

VITAMIN C

Vitamin C, or ascorbic acid, is necessary to maintain connective tissue. It also helps the body to absorb iron from the intestine and helps to heal wounds. It is also claimed that extra large doses of vitamin C helps to prevent or cure colds but there is little evidence to support this.

Sources
Sources of vitamin C are: blackcurrants, sprouts, cabbage, cauliflower, citrus fruits, strawberries, liver, peas, tomatoes, potatoes. Almost one-quarter of the recommended daily amount of vitamin C comes from potatoes. Although potatoes do not contain much vitamin C, we eat so many that they supply us with a substantial quantity of the recommended daily amount (see Fig. 4.6).

FIG. 4.6 Sources of vitamin C

Pure fruit juices are a good source of vitamin C but not fruit squashes unless they have been fortified with vitamin C.

Milk, meat, eggs, cereals and bread are all poor sources of vitamin C.

Vitamin C is easily destroyed by exposure to air, heating and in cooking water. To conserve as much vitamin C as possible when cooking vegetables, remember to:
1. Cook quickly in minimal quantities of water.
2. Prepare and cook vegetables just before required.
3. Do not use bicarbonate of soda in green vegetables as this increases losses.

Requirement

Like the B group vitamins, vitamin C is water soluble and is not stored by the body. We should therefore take adequate amounts of this vitamin per day. The recommended amount is 30 mg for adults and 20–30 mg for children. Pregnant and lactating women need 60 mg/day.

Deficiency

Deficiency in the UK is fairly rare, but can occur, especially in elderly people if they have poor diets. Deficiency leads to bleeding, especially in the gums, weakness, muscle and joint pain, poor wound healing and irritability. Prolonged deficiency leads to *scurvy*. This was common in sailors in the last century who did not take fruit and vegetables on sea voyages.

FAT-SOLUBLE VITAMINS

These are not lost in cooking and are stored by the body.

VITAMIN A

Vitamin A is essential for vision in dim light. It is required to form visual purple, a substance in the retina of the eye. It is also required for the maintenance of healthy skin and to keep mucous membranes moist.

Sources

The sources of vitamin A can be divided into two groups:
• Retinol – from animal sources: liver, kidney, butter, margarine, milk.
• Carotene – this is the yellow/orange pigment in fruit and vegetables. It can be converted in the body to retinol, especially ß-carotene. Sources of carotene are: carrots, tomatoes, dark-green vegetables (see Fig. 4.7).

Requirements

Recommended daily amounts (ROA) range from 300–725 μg for girls and boys aged 0–14. The ROA for adults is 750 μg/day and 1200 μg/day for lactating women.

About two years' supply of vitamin A is stored in the liver if an adequate diet has been taken. Excessive quantities of vitamin A can be toxic (poisonous) to the body and can eventually lead to death.

FIG. 4.7 Sources of vitamin A

Deficiency

A lack of vitamin A in the diet causes night blindness and will eventually lead to permanent blindness. This especially affects children in poor countries where the diet is deficient in vitamin A.

VITAMIN D

Vitamin D (cholecalciferol) assists in the absorption of dietary calcium from the intestine and in the deposition of calcium on cartilage to produce bone.

Sources

There are two sources of cholecalciferol:
- Dietary sources: fish liver oils, oily fish, egg yolk, margarine and butter, fortified breakfast cereals (see Fig. 4.8).
- Vitamin D is also obtained from the action of sunlight on dehydrocholesterol, a substance under the skin.

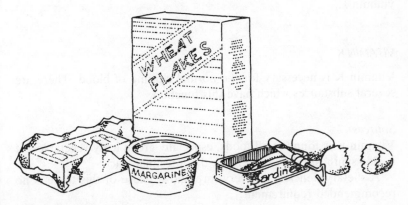

FIG. 4.8 Dietary sources of vitamin D

Requirement

Sunlight is the most important source of vitamin D for most people and so a dietary source is not required. Certain groups of the population, however, do not get adequate exposure to sunlight and require a dietary intake of the vitamin. Young children, and pregnant and lactating mothers require dietary vitamin D because they have increased requirements due to the formation of bones and teeth. The elderly, the housebound and Asian women and children who cover most of their skin also require dietary vitamin D.

Deficiency

In children a lack of vitamin D in the diet leads to the bone disorder *rickets*. The long bones do not develop fully, causing bandy legs, knocked knees and fragile bones.

The adult form of rickets is *osteomalacia*. This causes aching pains in joints and bone tenderness. It can also cause serious fractures even after a slight fall.

VITAMIN E

The exact function of vitamin E (tocopherol) is not clear. It can cause increased fertility in rats but not in humans.

Sources

Vitamin E is found in most foods; it is especially rich in vegetable fats, cereal germ and eggs.

Deficiency of vitamin E is unknown because it is so widely available. There are no recommended daily allowances for vitamin E.

VITAMIN K

Vitamin K is necessary for the normal clotting of blood. There are several substances which have this function.

Sources

Vitamin K is found in all foods, especially green leafy vegetables. It is also synthesised by bacteria in the intestinal tract.

A dietary deficiency is very rare and because of this there is no recommended requirement.

MINERALS

Minerals are required by the body for various functions:
• constituents of bones and teeth;
• constituents of body fluids;
• necessary to control body processes, e.g. transmission of nerve impulses, the release and utilisation of energy.

Most of the mineral elements can be detected in the body but only about fifteen are essential and must be obtained from food. These can be divided into two groups:

Major minerals: those required in fairly large amounts: calcium, iron, phosphorus, potassium, sodium, chlorine and magnesium.

Trace elements: those required in only minute quantities: iodine, fluorine, chromium, cobalt, copper, nickel and zinc.

MAJOR MINERALS

CALCIUM AND PHOSPHORUS

Calcium and phosphorus form calcium phosphate which is the material which gives strength and hardness to bones and teeth.

Calcium and phosphorus are the first and second (respectively) most abundant minerals in the body – both these minerals are found in the skeleton. Calcium is also required for blood clotting and the correct functioning of muscles and nerves.

Sources
Calcium: milk, cheese, bread (added by law to white bread), bones of canned fish, hard water (see Fig. 4.9).

Calcium is found in wholegrain cereals but absorption may be affected by the presence of *phytic acid* which binds the calcium and makes it unavailable to the body.

Phosphorus: present in nearly all foods especially cheese, peanuts and yeast extract. Phosphates are added to a lot of processed foods.

Requirement
The recommended daily amount for adults is 500 mg calcium daily. This will be provided by a daily consumption of less than 500 ml (1 pt) of milk. Growing children, and pregnant and lactating mothers need additional calcium for bone growth and development.

There is no estimated recommended daily amount for phosphorus.

FIG. 4.9 Sources of calcium

Deficiency

Symptoms of rickets (in children) and osteomalacia (in adults) may develop if the diet is lacking in calcium *and* vitamin D. Supplies of calcium in the UK diet are plentiful so a dietary lack is rare. A deficiency of phosphorus is unknown in man.

SODIUM, CHLORINE AND POTASSIUM

All body fluids contain sodium, chlorine (as sodium chloride or salt) and potassium. Salt is found in the extracellular fluids (e.g. blood), whereas potassium is present inside the cells (intracellular fluid).

These elements are involved in maintaining the water balance of the body; sodium is also essential for muscle and nerve activity.

All salt and potassium taken in the diet is absorbed and any excess is excreted by the kidneys and lost in urine. Salt is also lost in sweat. If the kidneys become diseased it may be necessary to restrict salt intake as this can cause water retention (oedema). Young babies have immature kidneys and so it is important not to add salt to any of their meals.

Sources

Salt: as table salt or as added to cooking. Added to processed foods, e.g. bacon, ham, cheese, stock cubes, tinned meat, fish and vegetables, bread and cereals (see Fig. 4.10).

Potassium: vegetables, fruit, meat and milk.

Requirement

All these elements are essential. In hot climates and in heavy industry salt is necessary as it is lost in sweat. In this country we eat

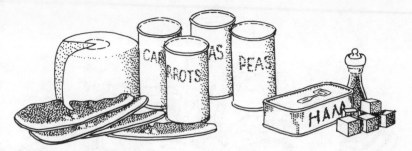

FIG. 4.10 Sources of salt

5–10 g salt daily; we require only 1 g/day. Because of its association with high blood pressure, we should cut down on our salt intake, especially by reducing the amount of salt sprinkled on food.

Deficiency
Very low salt intakes can cause muscle cramps. Deficiencies of potassium can occur in certain medical conditions.

IRON

Iron is a component of haemoglobin – the red pigment of blood. Haemoglobin transfers oxygen around the body to cells where it is required for the production of energy.

Sources
Sources of iron can be divided into two (see Fig. 4.11):
- *Haem sources*, i.e. those containing blood. These are the best sources of iron as they are easily absorbed and include all red meat, liver, kidney and corned beef.
- *Non-haem sources*, i.e. those not containing blood, including cocoa, chocolate, white bread (added by law), treacle, dried fruit, pulses, egg yolk, green leafy vegetables and fortified breakfast cereals. These are less well absorbed than haem sources of iron.
  Absorption is reduced by the presence of certain substances, e.g. phytic acid (found in wholegrain cereals), phosphate and egg. Absorption is increased by the presence of meat, vitamin C and folic acid.

Requirements
Red blood cells are continually destroyed and must be replaced. Some of the iron can be reutilised but we do need a daily supply of iron. Women require more iron than men because of regular men-

FIG. 4.11 Sources of iron

strual losses. Pregnant women need even more iron to supply enough for the development of the baby's blood.

Milk is a poor source of iron but babies are not deficient as they store enough iron in the liver to last for about 3 months.

Deficiency

A lack of iron in the diet leads to iron deficiency anaemia. This is the most common nutritional deficiency in the world and affects mainly women because of their extra needs. The symptoms of anaemia include: fatigue and inability to sustain physical effort – this is due to the reduced oxygen-carrying capacity of the blood; pale skin, fingernails and mucous membranes.

TRACE ELEMENTS

IODINE

Iodine forms part of the hormone *thyroxine* in the thyroid gland. (The thyroid gland is situated in the neck region.) Thyroxine helps to regulate metabolism.

Sources

Iodine is found in a wide range of foods. The quantity in vegetables and cereals depends on the level in soil. Iodine is also added to table salt.

Requirement

Only a minute quantity is required each day.

Deficiency
A deficiency of iodine causes the thyroid gland to swell in the neck, giving a *goitre*. This used to be common in areas of low soil iodine levels, e.g. Derbyshire and Switzerland.

FLUORINE

Fluorine is present in bones and teeth. It hardens the enamel on teeth and makes them more resistant to tooth decay.

Sources
Tea, seafood, and it is also added to the water supplies in some areas and to certain toothpastes.

Requirements
Fluorine may help reduce dental decay by strengthening the teeth of children. In areas where fluorine occurs naturally in the water supply the incidence of dental decay in children is reduced. Excessive fluorine may cause dark-brown spots or mottling of the teeth.

QUESTIONS

1. What are the functions of thiamin, riboflavin and nicotinic acid?
2. Which vitamins cause the following deficiency diseases: beriberi, scurvy, rickets?
3. What measures can be taken to reduce vitamin C losses in cooking?
4. List two groups of people who require extra calcium in the diet and explain why.
5. What are the sources of the following: vitamin A, vitamin D, iron, calcium, iodine?
6. What are the symptoms of iron deficiency?
7. Why do some people develop rickets?
8. Why is it beneficial for children to drink fluoridated water?

5

DIGESTION AND ABSORPTION

Food is necessary to maintain life, to promote growth and repair, and to produce energy. To enable us to use food in this way it must be swallowed and converted into simple forms which can be absorbed by the body. This is the process of digestion and absorption.

The whole process takes place in the *digestive tract*.

Digestion is the physical and chemical breakdown of food into simple forms.

Absorption is the movement of simple forms of food from the walls of the digestive tract into the bloodstream.

Excretion is the removal of any waste products and residue from digestion.

Although we eat to live most of us are fortunate in having enough food and we only eat food that looks and smells appealing. Food should therefore be presented in an attractive way to appeal to our senses of smell and sight. Food should also taste good. The taste, smell and sight of food influences our *appetite* and is affected by our surroundings and emotional state. This is particularly important for children and also for people with reduced appetites through illness. Appetite is less important if we are *hungry*. This is a complex sensation which occurs when the stomach is empty and levels of glucose and fatty acids are reduced in the blood (these are the body's energy stores).

Unfortunately a lot of appetising food, especially to children, is food that contains very few nutrients, e.g. sugary foods and drinks; these foods should be discouraged in children in order to prevent overweight and dental caries. More nutritious food should be presented in an appetising form.

THE PROCESS OF DIGESTION

The physical breakdown of food, i.e. breaking it into smaller pieces, occurs mainly in the mouth; it is necessary for food to be small enough to swallow.

The chemical breakdown of food, i.e. breaking it into smaller units, occurs throughout the digestive tract; during digestion glands produce 'digestive juices' which contain special substances known as *enzymes*.

Enzymes are found in all living matter and speed up chemical reactions. In the digestive tract various enzymes are produced which speed up the breakdown of food into smaller units, particularly into nutrients. Each enzyme is specific, i.e. one enzyme can work on one type of reaction only. There are, therefore, many enzymes in the digestive tract all involved in specific reactions. The action is illustrated in Fig. 5.1.

Figure 5.2 shows a diagram of the human digestive system.

$$\text{Food XY} \xrightarrow[\text{enzyme}]{\text{action of}} \text{X} + \text{Y}$$

FIG. 5.1

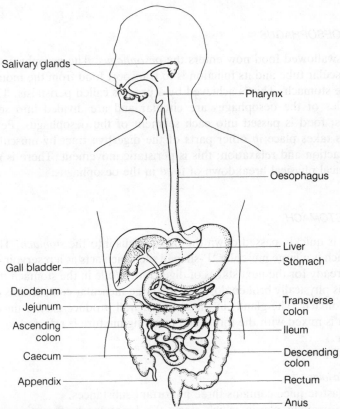

Salivary glands

Pharynx

Oesophagus

Liver

Stomach

Gall bladder

Duodenum

Jejunum

Transverse colon

Ascending colon

Ileum

Caecum

Descending colon

Appendix

Rectum

Anus

FIG. 5.2 The digestive tract

THE MOUTH

The digestive process begins in the mouth where food is physically broken down. This process is known as *mastication* and involves the cutting and grinding of food by the teeth into smaller pieces. Special *salivary* glands situated in the jaw area produce *saliva* which enters the mouth via ducts and moistens food. The *tongue* pushes food around the mouth to aid moistening and the action of the teeth, and also is necessary to aid swallowing.

Healthy teeth and gums are essential for mastication of solid food. Until a baby's teeth develop it is impossible to give him hard food because he will be unable to break the food into small enough pieces for swallowing. At weaning, and until the first teeth come through, babies are given soft semi-solid food.

Present in the saliva is the enzyme salivary amylase which starts the conversion of starch into maltose. No other chemical breakdown takes place.

THE OESOPHAGUS

The swallowed food now enters the *oesophagus*. The oesophagus is a muscular tube and its function is to transport food from the mouth to the stomach. This is achieved by a process called peristalsis. The muscles of the oesophagus are circular and are divided into segments; food is passed into each segment of the oesophagus. Peristalsis takes place in other parts of the digestive tract by muscular contraction and relaxation; this is peristatic movement. There is no chemical physical breakdown of food in the oesophagus.

THE STOMACH

Food is quickly passed down the oesophagus into the *stomach*. The stomach is a large muscular 'J'-shaped sac which acts as a reservoir of food ready for the next stages of digestion. While in the stomach the food is physically broken down by the large muscular contractions of the stomach. The glands in the stomach wall produce gastric juices which is mixed with the food. The resulting mixture is referred to as *chyme*.

Gastric juice
The gastric juice contains three important substances:
• The enzyme pepsin which starts the breakdown of proteins to smaller units of amino acids, called *peptides*. Rennin is present in

the gastric juice of young babies; it clots milk so that pepsin can work more effectively.

- Hydrochloric acid is present in the gastric juice; it destroys most of the bacteria which is present in food and supplies the acid conditions necessary for pepsin activity.
- The gastric juice also contains 'intrinsic factor' necessary for vitamin B_{12} absorption (see Ch. 4).

Food remains in the stomach for 2–4 hours; the exact time depends on the type of food eaten and the emotional state of the person. Fatty foods will remain in the stomach for longer periods than other foods, particularly foods such as rice.

Food leaves the stomach in small amounts and enters the small intestine, via the pyloric sphincter muscle.

THE SMALL INTESTINE

The small intestine consists of three distinct parts: the duodenum, the first part of the small intestine from the stomach; the jejunum and finally the ileum. It is the longest part of the digestive tract; being about 4 m in length. The main bulk of digestion and absorption takes place in this organ.

Secretions from the pancreas and gall bladder enter the duodenum and mix with chyme from the stomach. The secretion from the gall bladder is bile. Bile emulsifies or disperses fat globules into small droplets to enable fat digestion to take place.

The secretion from the pancreas, known as *pancreatic juice*, contains several enzymes for breaking down food. It is alkaline and neutralises the acid chyme.

The enzymes present in pancreatic juice and their function are as follows:

- Trypsin, formed from the activation of trypsinogen by enterokinase, continues the breakdown of proteins into peptones.
- Amylase converts undigested starch to maltose.
- Lipase breaks fat into fatty acids and glycerol; these are the building units of fat, therefore fat digestion is completed.

The ileum also produces a secretion known as 'intestinal juice'. This also contains enzymes and continues digestion.

- Peptides converts peptones to amino acids, the building units of protein, therefore completing protein digestion.

Intestinal juice contains various enzymes to break down carbohydrates to their building units.

- Maltase breaks down maltose to glucose.
- Sucrose breaks down sucrose to glucose and fructose.
- Lactase breaks down lactose to glucose and galactose.

After the food is digested in the small intestine, the smaller units can be absorbed into the bloodstream via the intestinal wall and used by the body. Absorption takes place mainly in the small intestine. The only foodstuff to be absorbed further up the digestive tract is alcohol which is usually absorbed in the stomach.

Structure of the small intestine

Food passes through the small intestine fairly slowly, taking about 2–3 hours. The walls of the small intestine have been specially adapted to facilitate maximum absorption of nutrients. Instead of having a flat surface, the walls are convoluted into thousands of finger–like projections, known as 'villi', illustrated in Fig. 5.3.

Each villus contains a single wall of cells which nutrients pass through. In the centre of each villus there is a lacteal which is connected to the lymphatic system. Blood capillaries surround each lacteal. Fatty acids and glycerol are absorbed into the lacteals. They reconvert to fat before entering the lymphatic system. Eventually fats enter the bloodstream as insoluble fat. Amino acids and monosaccharides are absorbed into the blood capillaries and enter the bloodstream.

Vitamins and minerals are also absorbed by the small intestine but they do not require any breakdown by enzymes.

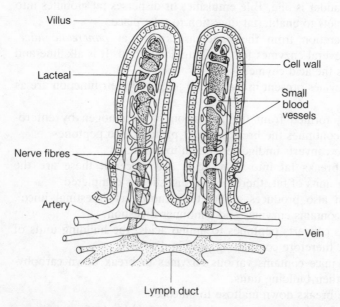

FIG. 5.3 Structure of intestinal villi

Coeliac disease

A small number of children are unable to absorb the food they eat because of damage to the small intestine, causing loss of villi and therefore absorptive surface. The agent causing the damage is the protein *gluten* found in wheat, barley, oats and rye and all products containing these cereals. This condition is known as *coeliac disease* and is often diagnosed when a baby is first weaned on to wheat-based cereals. As the food taken by the baby is unable to be absorbed, diarrhoea and weight loss result. A diet free of gluten results in the reappearance of villi with normal absorption and development.

THE LARGE INTESTINE

When the nutrients have been absorbed from food the residue is passed into the *large intestine*. The large intestine also consists of several sections, the caecum, the colon and the rectum. The anus is the opening of the rectum to the exterior.

In the caecum the food residues are in a liquid form, but water is absorbed all along the large intestine to form more solid food residues (faeces). As well as indigestible food residues faeces also contain debris from the continuous replacement of cells in the digestive tract. Bacteria normally present in the large intestine may continue the digestion and absorption of food residues. The large intestine stores the faeces until they are excreted via the anus. The faeces are propelled by mass movement. The time taken for expulsion depends on the amount of fibre taken in the diet. If the diet contains insufficient fibre small hard faeces are formed which move slowly down the large intestine and are difficult to pass. Such diets can also cause *constipation* (see Ch. 4).

A diet high in fibre forms bulky faeces which do not remain in the large intestine for prolonged periods and are easily passed. Foods rich in fibre include wholegrain cereals, fruit and vegetables (see Ch. 3).

The entire passage of food from mouth to anus can take 1–3 days, this can be increased dramatically by disease or prolonged by up to a week by lack of fibre in the diet.

THE FATE OF NUTRIENTS IN THE BODY

PROTEINS

During digestion, proteins are broken down to amino acids which enter the bloodstream via the small intestine. Amino acids are carried directly into the liver. As stated in Chapter 3, proteins are the only nutrient containing nitrogen, which is essential for growth and repair of tissues.

In the liver, the essential amino acids which have been absorbed are mobilised to other tissues and organs of the body where they are used for growth and repair. Non-essential amino acids can be made from other non-essential amino acids present in the liver. This process is known as transamination. Amino acids that are not required for growth and repair are split; the nitrogen-containing portion is removed by the liver, in a process called deamination. Urea is formed which is excreted in urine by the kidneys. The rest of the amino acid can be converted to glucose and used as a source of energy.

CARBOHYDRATES

The monosaccharides formed from carbohydrate digestion are absorbed into the bloodstream and enter the liver.

These may be then all converted to glucose and used directly for energy via a series of complex reactions or pathways. Carbon dioxide and water are also produced from these reactions.

Excess carbohydrate to energy requirements can be converted to glycogen, the storage carbohydrate in humans. Glycogen is stored in the liver and in muscle and can be used as a source of glucose when insufficient food is taken. When all the glycogen stores have been filled, excess carbohydrate will be converted to fatty acids and stored in the body as adipose tissue or body fat.

The level of glucose in the blood is carefully monitored. Excessive glucose in blood is transported to the tissues of the body with the aid of the hormone insulin, which is produced in the pancreas. Some children and adults fail to produce insulin and develop diabetes. The glucose levels in the blood rise until the excess is excreted by the kidneys. Children who develop diabetes usually require insulin injections as they normally stop producing insulin altogether. They need to regulate the amount of carbohydrate foods they eat and also need to eat regularly. Often adults who develop diabetes have a milder form which does not require insulin injections but still necessitates a modified diet.

FATS

Once absorbed into the lacteals in the villi of the small intestine fatty acids and glycerol re-form into fat. The fat is carried to the bloodstream via the lymphatic system. Fat is carried in blood as minute droplets which are often carried with amino acids. Fat can be converted in the liver to glucose and used as a source of energy by a series of complex pathways. Excessive levels of fat in the liver are deposited as adipose tissue.

QUESTIONS

1. Distinguish between the processes of digestion, absorption and excretion.
2. Write down what you have eaten for your last meal. Make a table showing how this food is digested and absorbed.

6

CHILDHOOD NUTRITION

A healthy diet in childhood lays the foundations of good health for life. If a child develops bad eating habits they will be difficult to break later on in life. Poor diet can lead to overweight and bad teeth in childhood and other conditions in adult life. Infants and children have increased requirements for many nutrients and these must be met if a child is to attain maximum mental and physical development.

INFANT FEEDING

BREAST-FEEDING

Breast-feeding is the best possible way of feeding a baby; not only is the composition of mother's milk more suited to her baby than cow's milk but there are also psychological advantages to mother and baby in the intimate contact of breast-feeding.

From the turn of the century to the mid 1970s there was a steady decline in the number of mothers breast-feeding their babies in Britain and other industrialised countries. This was due to social, psychological, economic, cultural and commercial reasons. After many years of experimenting, baby-milk manufacturers have decided that perhaps breast milk is best for babies after all! This, together with medical opinion and 'breast is best' pressure groups has reversed the trend, and now breast-feeding is becoming popular again, two-thirds of mothers now breast feed their babies.

It is better to breast feed a baby for at least a week or two if possible and mothers should be given every encouragement to breast feed. Ante-natal classes and midwives help to prepare the mother for breast-feeding. Breast milk is readily available, easily absorbed and economical. It is already sterilised and is always at the right temperature for the baby.

Composition of breast milk

The composition of breast milk gradually alters as the baby gets older. During the first few days of a baby's life the milk secreted by the breast is known as *colostrum*. This is a lemon, yellowish, translucent fluid which contains more protein, salts, fat-soluble vitamins and less lactose (milk sugar) and fat than fully established breast milk. The increased protein is mainly in the form of immunoglobulins; these proteins are found in the blood and help fight infection. The presence of these substances in colostrum help protect the baby's bowels against viruses and infection and against the development of allergies.

From about day 6 to day 10 the mother will produce 'transitional breast milk'. During this period the protein levels fall and the lactose content increases. From the tenth day onwards the mother produces 'mature breast milk'. Over several months mature breast milk gradually changes as the fat content rises to match the baby's increased energy requirement (see Table 6.1).

TABLE 6.1 Average composition of breast milk

Protein	1.3%
Fat	4.2%
Lactose	7.5%
Water	87.8%
Mineral salts	0.2%
Energy per 100 ml	70 kcal/293 kJ

Source: *The Composition of Mature Human Milk.*
DHSS Report on Health and Social
Subjects, No. 12, London, HMSO, 1977.

Requirement

The breast-fed baby will decide on his own individual needs; this is usually based on satisfying the baby's hunger, expressed by crying. A mother soon recognises the cry expressing hunger from other needs. A baby is having sufficient milk if he is contented, gaining weight and passing normal stools. After the first 2 days the stools of a breast-fed baby are yellow and have a porridge-like consistency.

Initially breast-feeding is introduced gradually by putting the baby to each breast for about 2 minutes at each feed for the first day, then 5 minutes on the second day, gradually increasing to 10 minutes to each breast. Usually mothers are advised to feed 'on demand'. During the first 5 months demand will fall from five to three feeds per 24 hours. After about 5 months if the baby is given the breast every time he cries the baby may develop a desire for the pleasure of feeding which may result in overfeeding and excessive weight gain.

BOTTLE-FEEDING

Sometimes it may be impossible to breast feed a baby due to various reasons, e.g. the mother may be taking certain drugs for medical conditions which are transferred to the milk and will be harmful to the baby, or it may be impossible to establish milk production, or, indeed the mother may find the idea of breast-feeding unacceptable.

The baby may have been born with a cleft palate so that sucking is impossible (although breast milk can be 'expressed' and fed to the baby with a spoon).

Whatever the reason, usually a substitute will have to be given and fed via a bottle.

Cow's milk, in the form of fresh, dried, condensed or evaporated, is unsuitable for young babies because it contains too much salt and protein. Young babies' kidneys are not fully developed and they are unable to cope with high salt intakes. If a baby cannot get rid of excess salt it can cause dehydration which is a serious condition in young babies. The excess protein in ordinary cow's milk can form curds in the stomach.

Cow's milk has to be modified so that it resembles human milk more closely. This is done by reducing the amount of protein and salt and by increasing the amount of lactose in the milk. Vitamins are also adjusted so that they are similar to the quantities found in breast milk. These modified milks are known as 'humanised baby milks'.

Guidelines have been published for manufacturers of infant milk formulae, and the DHSS's recommendations for quantities of major nutrients are given in Table 6.2.

Baby milks are available as dried powders or in ready to feed

TABLE 6.2 Recommended quantities of nutrients in infant milk formulae

Protein	1.2–2.0 g	
Fat	2.3–5.0 g	
Carbohydrate – total	4.8–10.0 g	per 100 ml
lactose	2.5–8.0 g	
Sodium	15–35.0 mg	
Energy	65–75 kcal/270–315 kJ	

Source: *Artificial Feeds for the Young Infant.* DHSS Report on Health and Social Subjects, No. 18, London, HMSO, 1980.

TABLE 6.3 Humanised dried milk

Modified	Highly modified
Cow & Gate Baby Milk Plus Ostermilk Complete Formula SMA	Cow & Gate Premium Osterfeed SMA Gold Cap

Note: It is safe to give babies ordinary liquid cow's milk and evaporated milk after 6 months.

bottles, although these are usually only available to hospitals (see Table 6.3).

Preparing the utensils
When bottle-feeding it is essential that the equipment used is scrupulously clean to protect the baby from infections, particularly gastro-enteritis.

Equipment can be sterilised by boiling bottles and teats in a large pan for at least 10 minutes. Another more popular and convenient method is to use chemical sterilisers. Several brands are available and consist of a large sterilising tank to which cold water is added and a sterilising tablet or solution. Firstly all bottles and teats should be thoroughly cleaned with a detergent, using a bottle brush for the inside of the bottles. Equipment is then rinsed thoroughly in clean running water, and then immersed into the sterilising tank, which has been filled with water and the correct quantity of sterilising solution or a tablet. The sterilisers usually have a floating lid to ensure that everything is kept under water (see Fig. 6.1). Usually

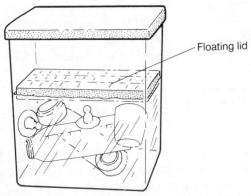

FIG. 6.1 A chemical steriliser, with a floating lid to ensure that all equipment remains under water

the equipment can be left in solution until required for use. It should be rinsed in boiled water before milk is added.

Preparing the feed

Follow the baby-milk manufacturer's instructions to ensure that the correct quantity of water and powder are used. Do not be tempted to add extra powder as this can cause dehydration as well as giving the baby too much energy.

1. The water used should be boiled and left to cool.
2. Wash hands well.
3. Rinse bottle with some of the boiled water – not tap water.
4. Fill bottle to the correct measuring mark with the boiled water.
5. Measure the exact amount of powder, using the scoop provided and levelling the powder with a knife (see Fig. 6.2).
6. Add to the water in the bottle.
7. Screw on the cap and shake well.
8. Bottles can be prepared in advance if they are refrigerated for no longer than 24 hours.

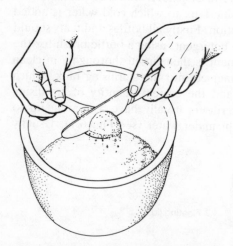

FIG. 6.2 Measuring the feed (Always measure the exact amount of powder, using the scoop provided. Level the powder with a knife.)

Feeding

1. Before starting to feed the baby, make sure the feed is not too hot, by letting a few drops drip on to the inside of the wrist; the feed should feel neither hot nor cold (see Fig. 6.3).
2. Make sure the baby is comfortable and has a dry nappy. Cuddle the baby, and have everything you need in easy reach, including

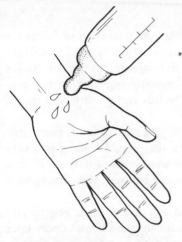

FIG. 6.3 Testing temperature of feed (Before starting to feed, make sure that the feed is not too hot, by letting a few drops drip on to the inside of the wrist. The feed should feel neither hot nor cold.)

a clean cloth to wipe spills. Tilt the bottle up so there is no air space for air to be sucked in with the milk; it is a good idea to interrupt the feed once or twice and hold the bottle upright to free the vacuum that forms so that sucking becomes easier.

Never leave a baby to feed alone, as the baby can choke.

Feeding routines

Demand feeding

This is giving the feed whenever the baby is hungry, and normally a regular schedule is adopted fairly soon; usually to five to six feeds daily by 3 weeks.

Premature and 'small for dates' babies may need small frequent feeds.

Often when a baby cries he may be thirsty and not hungry – cooled boiled water should be given in sterilised bottles. A little unsweetened fruit juice could be given to make the water more interesting.

VITAMINS

The DHSS recommends that multivitamin drops containing A, D and C should be given to babies:
• Breast-fed – 3 drops at 4 weeks, 7 drops at 4 months (full dose).
• Bottle-fed – 2 drops at 4 weeks, 4 drops at 4 months (full dose).

WEANING

'Weaning' is the term given to describe the transition of feeding a baby solely on milk to the gradual introduction of solid foods into the diet. This normally starts from 4 to 6 months. In the past babies have been weaned earlier than 4 months but this is not recommended, as early introduction of solids can predispose towards obesity.

Initially one or two teaspoons of smooth puréed foods (see Table 6.4) are given at one feed, or during the feed. Weaning is a very gradual process and initially the baby may refuse solids as this is a completely new experience. If solids are refused, then try again a few days later.

Do not add sugar to a baby's food as this can cause obesity and also gives a taste for sweet foods which can cause dental decay later on.

Do not add salt to savoury foods as at this stage a baby's kidneys are immature and they cannot cope with a heavy salt load.

A rice-based cereal is preferable initially as early introduction to wheat could precipitate an allergic reaction to gluten, a wheat protein.

TABLE 6.4 First weaning foods to use

Try one new food at a time, for about 3 days	
Fruit	Cooked and puréed dessert apples, pears, peaches or prunes without sugar
Vegetables	Cooked potato, carrots, cauliflower or green vegetables. Press through a sieve or liquidise with some of the vegetable water
Baby cereals	Use a rice-based cereal at first and mix it with breast milk or milk formula. Choose a sugar-free brand
Commercial baby foods	First stage strained foods are suitable. Jars and tins should only be kept for 24 hours in the refrigerator once opened

Spoon-feeding

A shallow, sterilised metal or hard plastic teaspoon should be used. Hold it close to the baby's lips so he can suck the food off. When the baby is happy doing this the spoon can be put into his mouth. Check that the food is not too hot before feeding. Allow the baby to feed at its own pace, not yours, even if this seems to be very slow.

Weaning should be introduced from 4 to 6 months to enable the baby to acquire the swallowing solid food reflex. Delay in weaning could result in difficulty in acquiring the reflex.

When the baby has been eating fruit, vegetables and cereals for 4 weeks, lean meat, egg yolk and fish can be given. As more solid food is taken, less milk is required, and the early morning and late evening feed can be abandoned (see Table 6.5).

TABLE 6.5 Feeding plan for 5–6 months

First feed	Breast or bottle feed
Breakfast	1–2 teaspoons of baby rice, occasionally lightly boiled egg yolk Breast or bottle feed
Lunch	1 tablespoon of puréed meat or fish (avoid tinned varieties) + 1 tablespoon sieved vegetables or potatoes Breast or bottle feed
Tea	1–2 teaspoons sieved unsweetened fruit or mashed banana Breast or bottle feed
Evening	Breast or bottle feed, if required

If the baby is thirsty in between meals, give cooled boiled water or well-diluted fruit juice.

Whole cow's milk or 'doorstep' milk can be given from 6 months. Skimmed milk should not be given until a child is 5 years old.

In addition to fruit, vegetables, baby cereals, meat, fish and egg yolk, from 6 months the following foods can be taken:
• Mild cheese – e.g. Edam, Cheddar, cottage or curd cheese. These can be grated or stirred into mashed potato, vegetables or home-made soup (salt-free).
• Beans, peas and lentils – can be mashed into vegetables.
• Natural yoghurt – can be mixed with fruit.
• Commercial baby foods can be given but it is cheaper to liquidise ordinary food before salt or sugar has been added.

From about 7–8 months minced or chopped foods can gradually replace the sieved and puréed foods. A baby will also be able to hold food in his hand, e.g. rusk, wholemeal bread, raw fruit or vegetables (washed and cut into pieces).

Well-cooked rice and finely chopped pasta can also be given, as can breakfast cereals. Avoid sugar-coated cereals and also muesli as this usually contains nuts (see Table 6.6).

TABLE 6.6 Feeding plan for 7–8 months

Early morning	Breast or bottle feed if continuing or diluted fruit juice or water
Breakfast	Cereal with milk, boiled egg with wholemeal toast fingers Breast or bottle feed or milk
Lunch	Minced meat, chicken, fish or cheese with mashed potato or vegetables Milk pudding or stewed fruit Milk or fruit juice
Tea	Sandwiches with a savoury filling Sliced fruit with yoghurt Breast or bottle feed
Bedtime	Breast or bottle feed or milk

By 7 months a baby should be able to drink from a cup; at 9 months a spoon will be held but the baby will not be feeding itself until about 15 months.

By the first birthday most family meals will be suitable, as long as they are chopped and do not contain excessive quantities of salt and sugar. A baby should have his meals with the rest of the family by this time.

Never leave a baby on its own to drink or eat in case of choking.

Sweet foods, including sweets, chocolate, cakes and biscuits are not essential in a child's diet; try and give them after a meal only. Babies still need 500 ml (1 pt) of milk a day until the age of 5.

Vitamin drops should be continued until the child is 2 years old.

PRE-SCHOOL-AGE CHILDREN

Meeting the nutritional needs of the pre-school-age child is very important as inadequate energy and nutrient content of the diet can lead to growth failure. Overeating, particularly of energy foods, can lead to obesity and sow the seeds for poor dietary habits in adulthood. Learning good eating habits in the under 5 is vital and the nursery nurse, either those looking after individual children or in a nursery school, can greatly influence a child's food choice and nutrient intake.

A low-fat/high-fibre diet recommended for the general population is not necessarily beneficial for the under 5s who need a certain amount of fat in their diet, otherwise energy needs may not

TABLE 6.7 Feeding plan for the under 5s

Breakfast	Unsweetened fruit juice Boiled egg Fingers of wholemeal toast Glass of milk
Main meal	Chicken casserole Mashed potatoes Peas Fruit jelly
Lighter meal	Sandwiches made from wholemeal bread with a savoury filling, e.g. tuna fish, ham, cottage cheese, grated cheese Tomato Fairy cake Slices of apple, glass of milk
Bedtime	Digestive biscuit, glass of milk

be met. This is certainly the case if refined carbohydrate foods are avoided. A high fibre intake can inhibit the bioavailability of calcium, iron and zinc (see Ch. 4), all required for growth. A careful balance between fibre and energy intake is necessary to avoid the extremes of over- and under-nutrition (see Table 6.7).

Children like a regular meal pattern especially with the rest of the family as this sets a routine – try and avoid sugary snacks in between meals.

NUTRITIONAL PROBLEMS OF PRE-SCHOOL-AGE CHILDREN

Poor eaters

A child's appetite is often variable; sometimes it may be difficult to tempt the child to eat anything, at other times it may be a struggle to satisfy the child's appetite. Such phases are a normal part of childhood and providing that they are healthy and active there is nothing to worry about.

When a child is not eating well their appetite can be tempted by presenting the food in interesting ways, e.g. fish-shaped fish cakes, faces made from meat, vegetables and potatoes, sandwiches cut into fancy shapes.

Children with small appetites do not like to be faced with large quantities of food. Small portions should be given. It is better for the child to ask for a second helping if he is still hungry.

Many children have strong likes and dislikes for food; a variety of tastes and textures of food should be introduced at an early age for the child to develop a sophisticated palate. If a child refuses certain foods once, they should be tried again later on; it is surprising how tastes can change over time.

If a child constantly refuses to eat certain foods which are essential for a well-balanced diet, they can be given in a disguised form. Table 6.8 lists some suggestions which can be tried.

TABLE 6.8 Ways of using disguising certain essential foods

Ways of using milk
Drinks – these can be flavoured and coloured using milk shake powders, drinking chocolate or malted milk powders
In milk puddings, blancmanges, egg custard, instant whips, yoghurt or ice-cream
Added to savouries – soups, mashed potatoes or as sauces for fish or vegetables

Ways of using cheese
Grated cheese sandwiches or as cheese on toast
Added to scrambled egg, mashed potato or sprinkled on to soups, vegetables and spaghetti
Cheese sauce to use with vegetables, fish and pasta

Ways of using eggs
In sandwiches (hard-boiled), boiled, poached, scrambled or as omelettes
Beaten into milky drinks, puddings or as egg custard
Beaten into mashed potato

Ways of using meat
As rissoles, beefburgers or sausages
As minced meat dishes, e.g. shepherd's pie, or added to soups

Ways of using vegetables
Mashed and mixed with mashed potato
Served with white or cheese sauce
As part of soups or stews

Do not substitute savoury foods with sweet foods or try and blackmail children into eating. Children soon learn that food can be an attention-getter. If a child refuses to eat it is better to appear totally unconcerned rather than to make a fuss and cause anxiety at mealtimes. If a child is going through a phase of food refusal it is a good idea to give vitamin drops.

Dental caries
See Chapter 2 for full details.
Dummy comforters filled with fruit syrups should most certainly be discouraged, even before a child's teeth erupt. Sticky toffees and

fruit gums should also be avoided in older children to prevent dental caries. Sweets should be confined to mealtimes and non-sugary foods should be given as snacks in between meals if the child is hungry.

Constipation
Some children develop constipation, especially if they are not eating many vegetables. Constipation can be cured by giving the child extra fluids, especially fruit juices, fruit or wholegrain cereals. Unprocessed bran may cause diarrhoea in small children and should be avoided.

Food allergies and intolerances
Very occasionally some children develop food allergies and intolerances, e.g. cows' milk or lactose intolerance, allergy to the wheat protein gluten (known as coeliac disease) or allergies to other foods, e.g. egg, chocolate. Symptoms of such allergies and intolerances range from diarrhoea and vomiting, 'failure to grow' and loss of appetite, lethargy, asthma to rashes. These require medical intervention. A special diet is indicated and dietary advice will be available from most hospitals by qualified dietitians.

SCHOOLCHILDREN

Children of school age (5–18) are growing and are active, and the recommended requirements for energy and nutrients reflect these. For teenagers the desired intakes of nutrients is higher than in adulthood, and the huge appetites of some children is a reflection of nutritional need, not just greed! Some children do not receive adequate nutrition, however, especially if they skip breakfast and make a poor choice of nutritional food at lunchtimes. Over-consumption of 'empty calories', particularly in the form of fat, sugar and sugary foods can cause obesity, dental caries and anaemia in older schoolgirls.

BREAKFAST

Studies have shown that schoolchildren who skip breakfast are more likely to be less alert and more accident-prone than those who do eat breakfast, particularly just before lunchtime.

Surveys have found that between 10 and 15 per cent of schoolchildren of all ages have nothing to eat at breakfast time; the proportion is higher in teenagers, but there are still around 8 per cent of 5–10-year-olds who go to school without anything to eat.

The traditional English breakfast of cereal, fried cooked breakfast of bacon, eggs, sausages, etc. is something most modern families do not have time for except on holiday, and certainly modern nutritional guidelines would not promote all the fat! Something to eat at breakfast, however, is beneficial, especially to younger children, particularly those attending school. A cereal-based breakfast, (especially a wholegrain cereal) and milk or wholemeal toast with milk to drink is a perfectly acceptable way to start the day. If a child refuses to eat anything at breakfast, do not force him to eat. In this case it may be better to let him have some fruit or cheese to eat at playtime instead.

SCHOOL MEALS

Before 1980 it was the duty of local education authorities to provide school meals for children which provided on average 880 kcal (3168 MJ) and 29 g protein, as the edible portion. Guidelines were also laid down as to the amount of fresh meat on the menu and also to preparation of food to ensure adequate supplies of vitamins and minerals.

The 1980 Education Act removed the statutory duties of education authorities to maintain nutritional standards; in fact there is no longer a statutory obligation for authorities to provide meals at all, except for those children entitled to free school meals.

Previously prices were controlled by the Government. Now individual education authorities can charge an appropriate price for food.

Infant and junior schools generally still provide a traditional two-course meal, but as there is no obligation to provide fresh meat or fish, convenience foods such as beefburgers and fish fingers are increasingly being used.

The main changes have occurred in secondary schools where the traditional school dinner is being replaced by a cash cafeteria service where children select items individually and pay individually. The main problem with this system is that many children are making nutritionally poor choices of food; for example, they may choose chips, a chocolate bar and a fizzy drink. If nutrient intake is poor for the rest of the day such children could be at risk.

Changes in the provision of school meals have also led to an increasing number of schoolchildren taking packed lunches to

TABLE 6.9 Nutritious packed meals

Tuna fish sandwiches (made from wholemeal bread)	Chicken leg
Tomato	Covered container filled with shredded cabbage, grated carrot, diced apple and chopped celery
Fruit yoghurt	Wholemeal bread roll
Shortbread biscuit	Crisps
Fruit juice	Pear
	Fruit juice
Oxtail soup	
Bread roll filled with cheese and cucumber	Ham and salad sandwiches
Banana	Muesli bar
Fruit juice	Fruit and jelly, set in individual covered containers
Homemade sausage roll	
Covered container filled with tomato, cucumber, celery	
Fairy cake	
Apple	
Fruit juice	

schools. Packed lunches should not be all carbohydrate. Table 6.9 gives some examples of nutritious packed meals for 5–10-year-olds.

QUESTIONS

1. Make a list of the advantages and disadvantages of breast- and bottle-feeding.
2. A 3-year-old child refuses to drink milk – how could you disguise it in dishes? Which foods could be adequately substituted?
3. Plan one week's packed lunches for an 8-year-old boy.

7

SPECIAL GROUPS IN THE COMMUNITY

PREGNANT AND LACTATING WOMEN

Extra demands are made on a woman's body during pregnancy and lactation so it is important that a woman is well nourished to ensure her and her baby's well-being. Often a pregnant woman develops an interest in healthy eating, but her diet should be good from the time of conception or even when she is planning her family.

Many malformations in the foetus develop at an early stage in pregnancy. Recent research has found that excess alcohol in the early weeks of pregnancy can cause defects and extra folic acid given in the early stages may be important in preventing neural tube defects (e.g. Spina bifida) in a small number of women.

Table 7.1 shows the recommended daily amounts of energy and nutrients during pregnancy and lactation and the percentage increase from the recommendations for non-pregnant women. It can be seen quite clearly that pregnancy does not involve eating for two! How-

TABLE 7.1 Recommended daily amounts of energy and nutrients in pregnancy and lactation

	Pregnancy	% increase	Lactation	% increase
Energy	10.0 MJ 2400 kcal	10	11.5 MJ 2750 kcal	22
Protein	60 g	10	69 g	27
Thiamin	1.0 mg	10	1.1 mg	20
Riboflavin	1.6 mg	25	1.8 mg	40
Nicotinic acid	18 mg	20	21 mg	40
Folic acid	500 µg	67	400 µg	50
Vitamin C	60 mg	100	60 mg	100
Vitamin A	750 µg	—	1200 µg	60
Vitamin D	10 µg	*	10 µg	*
Calcium	1200 mg	140	1200 mg	140
Iron	13 mg	8	15 mg	25

* No dietary sources necessary in women who receive sufficient sunlight.

Source: Recommended Daily Amounts of Food Energy and Nutrients for Groups of People in the United Kingdom, London, HMSO, 1979.

ever, if a mother's diet is inadequate, the foetus will receive the nutrients, not the mother. In countries where food supplies are poor, this can drastically affect the health of the mother.

The average weight gain during pregnancy is 12.5 kg (28 lb). Most of the weight gain is from the foetus itself. Extra uterus (womb) and breast tissue also develop. About 4 kg (9 lb) of the gain is in the form of fat. This acts as an extra energy store for breast-feeding.

One other important factor to be considered is smoking. All smoking is detrimental to health, and in pregnant women it is doubly so.

EXTRA NUTRIENT NEEDS

Energy

Extra energy is required for the growth of the foetus but often a mother becomes less active during pregnancy; the recommendation is for a 10 per cent increase only during pregnancy. This increases to 22 per cent during breast-feeding as extra energy is recommended for milk production.

If a pregnant woman's weight is increasing too rapidly the energy intake can be restricted to about 6.3 MJ (1500 kcal). Energy intakes below this figure are not recommended.

Protein

As the intake of protein is very high in the UK it is usually not necessary for a pregnant or lactating woman to eat any more protein foods than normal. More protein will be consumed, however, from the extra milk taken for the increased calcium recommended.

Vitamins

Milk, fruit and vegetables can supply the extra requirements for vitamins. Citrus fruits or fresh fruit juices should be taken daily for extra vitamin C. Oily fish, egg yolk, margarine and fortified breakfast cereals should be taken for vitamin D. Usually pregnant women are given folic acid supplements by their GP in the last 3 months of pregnancy.

Minerals

The recommended daily amount for calcium is 140 per cent more during pregnancy and lactation, which is needed for bone development of the foetus during pregnancy and milk production in lactation; 500 ml (1 pt) of milk or equivalent (e.g. yoghurt, cheese) should be taken each day.

Insufficient calcium in the diet can result in a removal of calcium from the mother's bones and teeth to be passed to the foetus.

If the mother is gaining too much weight skimmed milk can be taken instead of whole milk as it contains the same amount of calcium.

The extra iron is needed for blood formation and can be met by eating plenty of red meat, especially liver and kidney, green vegetables, bread and iron-fortified breakfast cereals. Usually iron supplements are given to pregnant women by their GPs, because lack of sufficient iron in the diet can result in anaemia (see Ch. 4).

Fluid intake

This should be increased during lactation, usually to match the amount of milk produced.

Alcohol intake should be reduced to a maximum of one drink per day during pregnancy as alcohol can cause deformities.

MORNING SICKNESS

This is quite common during the early stages of pregnancy and can occur at any time of the day. Usually small, light, frequent meals and dry biscuits or toast spread with jam or honey relieves the symptoms.

INDIGESTION AND HEARTBURN

These often occur in the late stages of pregnancy as the womb exerts pressure on the stomach. The 'burning' sensation of heartburn can be reduced by taking small frequent meals, avoiding fatty or highly seasoned or spiced foods or any foods found to be irritating.

CONSTIPATION

This is very common throughout pregnancy and can cause considerable discomfort. Constipation occurs because of hormonal changes causing a loss of muscle tone in the intestines so that the movement of food is reduced. Increasing the amount of fibre (see Ch. 3) in the diet and the amount of fluid will normally remedy this problem.

A healthy diet during pregnancy and lactation would include:

Extra milk	For calcium, protein
Extra red meat especially liver, kidney, fortified breakfast cereals, bread	For iron

Extra citrus fruits, green
vegetables

For vitamin C, folic acid

Extra fibre – wholemeal bread,
fruit, vegetables, grainy cereals

To prevent constipation

Extra fluid

For breast-feeding

Fatty foods and sugary foods are best reduced to prevent excessive weight gain.

VEGETARIANS

Vegetarians are people who do not eat meat. The reasons why they do not eat meat are varied. There are two types of vegetarians.

LACTO-VEGETARIANS

The majority of vegetarians are lacto-vegetarians. They do not eat meat or fish but they will eat milk, cheese, eggs and butter as well as fruit, vegetables, nuts and cereals. It is not difficult to provide them with a good diet as they have a variety of foods to choose from (see Table 7.2).

TABLE 7.2 Sample menus for vegetarians

	Lacto-vegetarian	Vegan
Breakfast	Fruit juice Muesli and yoghurt	Fruit juice Muesli and soya milk
Lunch	Lentil soup and wholemeal roll Fresh fruit	Lentil soup and wholemeal roll Fresh fruit
Evening meal	Cheese and onion pie Salad Fruit crumble Custard	Cashew nut risotto Salad Fruit crumble (made with vegetable margarine) Custard (made from soya milk)

VEGANS

Vegans are very strict vegetarians who will not eat any food at all from animal sources: no meat, fish, cheese, butter, lard, suet or dripping. All their food has to come from plants. Their meals are based on beans, peas, lentils, nuts, rice, flour and other cereals, fruit and vegetables. The complete lack of meat and dairy foods makes it very difficult to plan meals for vegans and to provide a balanced diet, especially for growing children who usually rely on these foods to provide the nutrients required for normal growth (see Table 7.2).

VEGETABLE SOURCES OF PROTEIN

Protein is found in small amounts in plant foods; it is of low biological value (i.e. it does not contain all the essential amino acids in the correct quantities required by man). Deficiencies of amino acids can be made good by 'complementation'. This is choosing plant protein foods from a variety of sources so that they complement each other. Mixtures of the following sources should therefore be taken:
- pulses, e.g. peas, beans (all types) and lentils;
- nuts;
- cereals, including bread;
- textured vegetable protein (TVP) made from soya beans.

VITAMIN B$_{12}$

This vitamin is found only in animal foods. Vegans, however, do not appear to develop anaemia from a deficiency because it is synthesised by bacteria in the gut.

MINORITY GROUPS

ASIANS AND THEIR FOOD

Religion is an important factor in determining the diet of people from Asia. So is the area from which the person originates; for example, people from Bangladesh are likely to be accustomed to fish whereas people from Pakistan are not. People from the Punjab eat chapati as their staple starch, those from Bangladesh eat rice and those from the state of Gujarat eat both.

It is perfectly possible to be well nourished on a traditional 'Asian' diet. However, some Asians in this country are not eating a balanced diet. This may be because they are not familiar with local substitutes for foods which are unavailable or because in a family on a tight budget, most of the animal protein foods go to the adult males.

SPECIAL BELIEFS ABOUT FOOD

Some foods are thought to either heat or cool the body; this has nothing to do with the temperature of the food or its spiciness.

'Hot' foods are: brown sugar, carrots, chilli, dates, eggs, aubergine, fish, ginger, honey, lentils, meat, onions, tea.

'Cold' foods are: cereals, chickpeas, most fruits, dairy produce, nuts, potatoes, most vegetables, sugar.

These beliefs are of no great importance ordinarily, but during pregnancy, illness and other times of physiological stress more attention is paid to these beliefs. Hot foods are avoided during pregnancy and when feverish, and cold foods when suffering from colds, coughs and when breast-feeding.

ASIAN RELIGIONS

Islam

The majority of Muslims come from the Indian sub-continent although there is a sizeable number of Muslims from the Arab world living in the UK. For a Muslim, religion, law and social organisation form an inseparable world which governs not only religious practice but social relationships, diet and hygiene.

Islamic customs forbid pork products and alcohol and insist on the ritual slaughter of meat, 'halal'. Only fish with fins and scales are eaten. During the month of Ramadan, Muslims fast between dawn and dusk, although children are exempt. Traditionally the men eat first and the women and children eat later unseen by the men, but this tradition is becoming more relaxed.

Hinduism

Hinduism has developed over thousands of years and is founded on a belief of non-violence and reincarnation. Hindus refuse to take life, therefore most are vegetarians. There is also a caste system in the Hindu faith. Castes vary in the degree of strictness with which they follow dietary and other laws.

The cow is a sacred animal and its slaughter is forbidden in India. Some less orthodox Hindus will eat lamb, chicken or pork, and white, but not oily fish. Very orthodox Hindus, particularly women, will not eat eggs since they are potentially a source of life.

Most Hindus rely on pulses, milk, yoghurt, buttermilk and home-made curd cheese for their protein. Their staple cereal is wheat, made into chapatis, but they also eat rice.

Many devout Hindus, particularly women and the elderly, fast on one or two days per week. They do not necessarily abstain from food entirely but eat only foods considered to be pure, e.g. milk, fruit, nuts, potatoes and yoghurt.

Sikhism

Sikhism developed from Hinduism and Islam and was founded 600 years ago by Guru Nanak. Sikhs do not eat beef but they may eat pork. Generally, Sikhs take a liberal view of diet and easily adapt to new surroundings. They are mainly meat-eating; few are vegetarians.

JUDAISM

Many Jewish people have been born and brought up in this country and are obviously very familiar with British foods.

Jewish food laws (Laws of Kashrut)
- Meat and milk foods must be kept apart in cooking and eating.
- Only the meat of animals that have a cloven hoof and chew the cud is permitted, e.g. not pig.
- Birds of prey may not be eaten.
- Animals and birds are slaughtered in a special way and then 'koshered', i.e. salted and steeped in water to remove all blood.
- Fish which have fins and scales are permitted, shellfish is forbidden.

THE SICK AND CONVALESCING

People who are ill or who are recovering from illness (convalescing) are a special group nutritionally as:
- they may have increased demands for several nutrients;
- they may have reduced appetites, especially children.

NUTRIENT REQUIREMENTS

Specific requirements during various illnesses are not known but generally patients with raised body temperatures will need extra fluid to replace losses from sweating. Protein requirements may be increased, especially if the patient has undergone surgery or is feverish. Extra vitamin C aids wound healing; extra fruit juice or citrus fruit given after surgery will aid recovery.

APPETITE

Usually people who are ill, especially children, lose their appetite for food. As their requirements are increased it is important to try and tempt patients to eat a well-balanced diet. Meals that are attractively served will tempt the patient, e.g. a funny face or picture for children. Small portions that do not overface are preferable. Six small meals served frequently during the day is a more acceptable meal pattern than three large meals.

Food given to patients should be light and not cause indigestion or heartburn. Fried and fatty foods, rich heavy puddings and highly spiced foods are best avoided.

Table 7.3 shows the foods to choose for a light diet; the food served to patients does not need to be sloppy or overcooked. To increase protein intake milky drinks or supplements, e.g. Complan and Build-up, can be given in between meals.

TABLE 7.3 Foods suitable for a light diet

Beverages: all
Biscuits: all
Bread/scones: all but avoid fresh or hot bread
Cake: plain only
Cereals: all
Cheese: suitable as long as it does not cause indigestion
Eggs: not fried
Fats: in moderation only
Fish: not fried or oily
Fruit: avoid tough skins
Meat: cook simply
Milk: encourage plenty
Preserves: all
Puddings: not rich pastry or suet
Sauces/gravies: not highly seasoned
Soups: suitable
Vegetables: not fried

An example of a day's meals for a sick child is shown below:

Breakfast	Fruit juice
	Lightly baked egg
	Wholemeal toast soldiers
	Weak tea
Mid-morning	Glass of Build-up
Lunch	Grilled fish fingers, mashed potatoes, peas and carrots presented as a train
	Fruit yoghurt

Mid-afternoon	Glass of milk
Evening meal	Small ham sandwich
	Fruit in jelly
Bedtime	Cup of hot chocolate
	Digestive biscuit

CHILDREN REQUIRING THERAPEUTIC DIETS

Occasionally when a child is ill, he may need to eat certain foods or avoid others in order to improve his condition. Such diets are prescribed by a doctor; information and help regarding therapeutic diets is obtainable from qualified dietitians, who are usually based in hospitals.

CHILDHOOD ILLNESSES REQUIRING DIETARY MODIFICATION

Cow's milk protein/lactose intolerance
Occasionally babies may be intolerant to modified baby milks; diarrhoea and failure to grow are the main symptoms. Special soya-based milks are available on prescription following diagnosis of this intolerance.

Inborn errors of metabolism
These are very rare and are usually associated with failure to utilise an amino acid or carbohydrate. The diet is very involved and requires the advice of a dietitian specialising in childhood disorders.

Coeliac disease
This is an allergy to gluten, a protein found in wheat, barley, oats and rye. All foods containing these cereals must be completely avoided. Gluten-free varieties of bread, biscuits, pasta, etc. are available on prescription after diagnosis.

Diabetes mellitus
If a child is diagnosed as having diabetes he will normally require injections of insulin and a controlled carbohydrate intake. Diabetes in childhood is the failure of the pancreas to secrete insulin (a hormone) which regulates blood sugar. A child needing insulin injections will need to eat a specific amount of carbohydrate at regular intervals to prevent blood sugar levels from rising too high or dropping too low. The diet is also normally high in fibre and low in fat. Each diabetic's diet is individual and is worked out by a dietitian.

QUESTIONS

1. Plan a day's menu for a pregnant mother.
2. What is the difference between a lacto-vegetarian and vegan?
3. Suggest ways of making a sick child's meals look attractive.

SPECIMEN ANSWER TO QUESTION 1

A day's menu for a pregnant woman

Breakfast	Unsweetened orange juice
	Bowl of muesli
	Wholemeal toast
Snack	Digestive biscuit
Lunch	Wholemeal bread filled with corned beef and salad
	Fruit cake
	Banana
Snack	Crackers and cottage cheese
Evening meal	Chicken and vegetable casserole
	Baked potatoes
	Apple pie made with wholemeal pastry
	Custard
Bedtime	Digestive biscuits
	Milky drink
Over the day	500 ml milk

8

FOOD POISONING, HYGIENE AND PRESERVATION

FOOD POISONING AND HYGIENE

Food should be handled and prepared as hygienically as possible to prevent contamination and food poisoning. This is especially important when the food is to be eaten by children, who have reduced resistance to infection.

There are three types of food poisoning: (1) chemical; (2) biological; (3) bacterial.

Chemical food poisoning can be caused by agricultural chemicals e.g. *insecticides, pesticides*. These are used by the farmer to ensure good crop yields. They are normally applied to the crop well before harvesting as they are toxic, but traces can remain in food. Normally chemicals in use are very thoroughly tested and cannot be used indiscriminately.

Chemical pollutants from industrial waste can also cause poisoning, especially if the waste is poured into rivers and the sea when fish, later caught for human consumption, can ingest the chemicals.

Biological food poisoning is caused by eating plants which contain toxic substances, normally by accident, e.g. eating poisonous mushrooms. It is important that children do not eat wild fungi or berries as these may be lethal.

Bacterial food poisoning is the most common type of food poisoning and can easily be avoided in the home if food is handled and prepared hygienically. The majority of food poisoning cases occur outside the home in large catering establishments. Laws exist to protect consumers and to ensure hygienic practices in catering establishments, but food poisoning by bacteria can occur in the home.

Bacteria are microscopic forms of life which cannot be seen by the naked eye. They are found everywhere – in the air, in water, in soil, plants, food, on animals and humans and in sewerage. There are many different types of bacteria, some of which are harmful and can cause poisoning.

The harmful bacteria can only cause poisoning if they are allowed to multiply in large numbers in food, which is then eaten. When the living bacteria enter the digestive tract they are normally killed, releasing a toxin or poisonous substance. Alternatively, some bacteria produce a toxin in food which is poisonous to the body if eaten. Most food-poisoning bacteria require warm, moist, airy conditions for growth and a good source of protein and carbohydrates. Badly stored and handled food, especially meat and dairy products, are ideal for rapid multiplication. Food-poisoning bacteria do not spoil the food and therefore it still looks and tastes wholesome.

It is important that bacteria should not be transferred on to food by unclean practices. In the home, the person handling food can ensure that food is clean and prepared hygienically by paying attention to:
- buying food;
- storing food;
- personal hygiene;
- kitchen and equipment hygiene.

BUYING FOOD

- Buy food from clean reputable shops.
- Make sure assistants do not touch food, especially food that will not be cooked before consumption.
- Make sure that perishable foods are refrigerated and covered and that fresh meat is separated from cooked meats.
- Do not buy food from shops where there are animals.
- Do not buy food that has passed its sell-by date, or best-before date.

STORING FOOD

- Refrigerate all perishables – e.g. dairy foods, meat, salad vegetables. Use cling film or plastic containers to protect against flies and the absorption of smells.
- Keep all other fresh foods in a cool place and use rapidly.
- Use canned and dried foods within the best-before dates.
- Cool left-over foods quickly and eat within 24 hours, or freeze as soon as cool.

PERSONAL HYGIENE

Bacteria are naturally present on humans, in our hair, noses, throats, on hands and in cuts and spots. In these places they are harmless but if ingested in large quantities they can cause poisoning. To avoid the contamination of food from human sources, before preparing food:

- Tie hair back, wash hands and scrub nails.
- Wear a clean apron.
- Always wash hands after visiting the toilet.
- Never cough, spit, sneeze or smoke over food. Do not prepare food if you have a heavy cold or have diarrhoea and vomiting.
- Cover any cuts, grazes, etc. with a waterproof dressing.
- Never lick spoons or fingers and then touch food with them.

KITCHEN AND EQUIPMENT HYGIENE

- Keep the kitchen clean by regularly washing work surfaces, the cooker and the floor, using separate cloths than those used for washing equipment, cutlery and crockery.
- Rinse out dishcloth after use and allow to dry in the air. Wash out in disinfectant regularly or use disposable cloths.
- Wipe up spills as soon as they occur.
- Do not allow pets on work surfaces. Keep separate utensils and dishes for pets. Do not allow small children to eat from pet dishes – pets carry bacteria and viruses which can cause illness in children.
- Make sure that all food sediments are removed from cutlery and crockery when washing up. Hot water and a good detergent ensure clean dishes.
- Make sure that all frozen food is thawed out thoroughly before cooking, particularly poultry. If food is not fully thawed out in the centre the cooking will only warm the food, making it an ideal medium for bacterial growth, leading to poisoning when eaten.
- Refuse should be removed from pedal bins in the kitchen daily and they should be regularly disinfected. Food waste should be wrapped. Dustbins should be kept well away from the kitchen and have a tight-fitting lid to protect from flies, cats and vermin.

FOOD SPOILAGE AND PRESERVATION

All the food that we eat was once living; some foods, e.g. meat and fish, are killed before being distributed to the consumer: other foods, e.g. fruit and vegetables, are distributed in the living state. As soon as food is slaughtered or harvested, it begins to deteriorate

and eventually will be unfit for consumption. Food spoilage is caused by two distinct processes:
- Self-destruction or natural decay within the food.
- Attack by micro-organisms causing alteration in the flavour, colour and smell of food.

Bacteria, moulds and yeasts can all spoil food.

Today we consume a wide variety of food from all parts of the world; most foods we eat are available throughout the year. To achieve this it is necessary to have ways of preserving food from spoilage so that it is fit to eat. Many methods of food preservation are centuries old, e.g. salting and drying. Other methods have only been developed in the last 100 years – e.g. canning, freezing, use of chemicals. Some preservation techniques create new foods, e.g. bacon, pickles, jams.

FOOD SPOILAGE

Self-destruction of food is caused by the natural loss of moisture and enzyme action. Fruit and vegetables readily lose moisture through leaves and skins and become smaller, limp and their skins become wrinkled. Meat, fish and cheese also lose moisture and become leathery in appearance and texture.

Enzymes naturally present in foods will cause spoilage following harvesting, e.g. the browning of fruit if it is cut or bruised, is caused by enzymes. The addition of acid, e.g. lemon juice, destroys the enzyme and stops browning.

Microbial spoilage

Bacteria, yeasts and moulds will also spoil food and make it inedible.

Bacteria present in milk eventually cause milk to sour. Some bacterial spoilage is desirable; for example, acid-producing bacteria convert cabbage to sauerkraut.

Moulds are microscopic plants which grow as fine threads. These can extend to form complex networks which are visible to the naked eye. Moulds need oxygen to grow and because of this are usually only found on the surface of many types of foods, particularly bread, cheese and fruit. Moulds can produce toxic substances that can penetrate inside food. If food has gone mouldy, it is safer to discard it totally rather than just cutting the surface mould away.

Yeasts occur naturally on the surface of fruits. They are also present in the air and in soil and multiply by 'budding'. This is the formation of a small bud which grows in size and eventually will detach itself from the parent cell. Yeasts 'ferment' sugars present in foods to produce carbon dioxide and alcohol. This is desirable when the yeasts on grape skins ferment the fruit sugars to wine, but can cause spoilage when, for example, jams and fruit yoghurts ferment.

FOOD PRESERVATION

Methods of food preservation aim to destroy or inhibit the substances that cause spoilage. This can be done by either killing the micro-organisms and enzymes present in food and storing in sterile conditions or by creating an environment which prevents growth and multiplication. Most food preservation methods are carried out commercially but domestic preservation is possible. Any food preservation process should also aim to retain the quality of the food as far as possible, e.g. by maintaining its nutritional value, colour, flavour and texture.

Preservation methods
Food can be preserved by:
• Heat treatment to reduce or completely destroy micro-organisms and enzymes, e.g. pasteurisation, sterilisation and by canning.
• Removing moisture, i.e. dehydration to inhibit micro-organisms.
• Lowering the temperature to inhibit micro-organism growth and enzyme activity, e.g. freezing.
• Addition of chemicals to inhibit micro-organism growth and enzyme activity, e.g. jam making, pickling.

DOMESTIC PRESERVATION OF FOODS

Refrigeration
Micro-organisms do not multiply rapidly in cold temperatures; food can be preserved for short times if stored in a domestic refrigerator at 5 °C. This temperature will allow slow multiplication of micro-organisms so refrigerated food will not have a long storage life. Enzyme activity still continues, also at a slow rate, and so there is also a loss of quality in refrigerated food. However, the benefit of refrigeration is that a few days' supply of fresh foods can be purchased at once, therefore eliminating the need to shop daily.

Storing food
Food should be wrapped before placing it in a refrigerator as food will lose moisture at low temperatures and dry out if not covered.

Some foods will also absorb odours from strongly smelling foods, changing the flavour of the food.

Cling film or plastic containers can be used to wrap food although meat and fish often develop off-flavour and discolour if cling wrapped. It is better to store meat or fish in glass or a ceramic dish so there is a layer of air surrounding the food.

The temperature inside the refrigerator varies in different areas. The ice box is the coldest and is usually marked by a star rating to indicate how long frozen food can be kept in it. The ice box should not be used to freeze food.

Star rating		Storage
* −	6 °C (21 °F)	Up to 1 week
** −	12 °C (10 °F)	Up to 1 month
*** −	18 °C (0 °F)	Up to 3 months

The warmest part of the fridge is the door, and also the bottom of the cabinet which is normally used to chill salad vegetables. Raw meat should always be stored *below* cooked foods to prevent contamination from any drips on to the cooked food.

Freezing

The principles of freezing are really just an extension of refrigeration; keeping food at 5 °C in a domestic refrigerator keeps food fresh for a longer but limited time; if food is kept at lower temperatures, as in a deep freeze, the food will remain wholesome for much longer. This is because the micro-organisms present in food cannot multiply and cause spoilage, also the natural deterioration of food is halted, particularly that of fruit and vegetables.

During the freezing process, the water found in foods is frozen to ice. As water expands when it is frozen, freezing can damage food texture because the ice crystals can rupture the cell wall so that the structure is lost when the food is thawed. This occurs especially in frozen fruits and vegetables which have a high water content, e.g. strawberries and courgettes. Frozen food is of a higher quality if the food is frozen very quickly at low temperatures as small ice crystals are formed which do less damage to cells. Quick freezing methods are only available commercially, but most foods can be successfully frozen at home.

Home freezing

Most home freezers operate at −18 °C (0 °F). Usually home freezers also have a 'fast freeze' switch which lowers the temperature to about −24 °C (−12 °F) this is used when large quantities of food are to be frozen, and needs to be turned on 2–3 hours before the food is placed in the freezer. Many cabinet-type freezers also have a special section for freezing food. Food that is purchased already frozen can be placed in the freezer at the operating temperature without switching on to fast freeze.

Freezing food

Almost any food can be frozen but for best results good quality food only should be frozen. Cooked food and dishes can be frozen successfully and it is economical to cook in bulk and freeze those items not required immediately. Baked goods such as bread, cakes, pizzas and pies freeze well, as do stews and casseroles and soups. When freezing cooked food it is important to cool the food quickly to prevent multiplication of bacteria. *Never* put hot or warm food into a freezer as this will raise the temperature. All food for freezing should be prepared as hygienically as possible because freezing does not kill micro-organisms, it merely renders them dormant; contaminated frozen food will still be contaminated when thawed.

Some foods do not freeze well; these include fresh fruit and vegetables, cooked whole potatoes, pasta and rice, whole eggs and milk puddings.

Previously frozen food should not be refrozen after thawing as flavour and texture deteriorate and change condition when thawed.

Table 8.1 lists the foods suitable for freezing and the preparation necessary, and Table 8.2 the recommended storage time.

Packaging materials

Food to be frozen should be well packaged to retain quality. Poorly packed food can dry out and develop 'freezer burn', and colour can also deteriorate. Frozen foods can also pick up flavours of other foods, as they can in the refrigerator.

• Bags – usually polythene and should be fairly thick; bags made specially for the freezer are available. Ordinary polythene bags can split at low temperatures. Bags are useful for wrapping awkward shapes and holding liquids. They should be tied with a wire twist and labelled. Some freezer bags have a white strip to allow marking with a pen.

Boil-in-bags are tough bags and allow food to be plunged straight into boiling water straight from the freezer.

Liquid foods can be poured into polythene bags standing inside a box. This can be sealed, labelled and frozen. Once frozen the box can be removed; the liquid is therefore frozen in a convenient shape for storing.

TABLE 8.1 Preparation of food for freezing

Fruit
The following methods can be used to freeze raw fruit:

Dry freezing	Used for fruit to be made into pies or preserves, and for currants, blackberries, strawberries and gooseberries. Wash, dry on kitchen paper, pack into rigid containers. Fruit can be frozen on a baking sheet and then packed so the fruit is free flowing
Freezing in sugar	Layer caster sugar and fruit (especially summer fruits) in rigid containers
Freezing in syrup	Used for fruits that discolour on freezing, e.g. peaches, apricots, pears. Use 300 ml syrup (sugar dissolved in water) to each 450 g fruit. Add syrup to fruit when cold. Ascorbic acid can be added to syrup to prevent discolouration

Vegetables
Freeze only freshly picked vegetables. Blanching is necessary to inactivate enzymes. Cool vegetables, pack in rigid containers and freeze or freeze on a baking sheet and then pack

Blanching	place vegetables in a wire basket and plunge into a pan of boiling water for the recommended time (see below) Plunge into ice-cold water, drain and pack

	Blanching time (mins)
Asparagus	2 mins (thin) – 4 mins (thick)
Aubergine	4 mins
Beans – French whole	2 mins
runner, sliced	1 min
broad	2 mins
Broccoli	3–4 mins
Carrots	3–5 mins
Cauliflower	3 mins
Corn on the cob	4 mins (small) – 8 mins (large)
Courgettes	1 min
Leeks	2–4 mins
Onions	2 mins
Parsnips	2 mins
Peas	1 min
Peppers	3 mins
Spinach	2 mins
Turnips	2 mins

TABLE 8.2 Storage times of frozen foods

	Storage time (months)
Meat (uncooked)	
Lamb	6
Beef	8
Pork, mince, offal, tripe	3
Bacon, vacuum packed	5
Bacon joints	1
Sausages	2
Poultry	
Chicken	12
Duck	6
Game	6
Fish	
White	3
Oily	2
Cooked dishes, pies, casseroles	3
Vegetables	12
Fruit	12
Unstoned fruit	3
Fruit pies	6
Baked goods	
Cakes, bread, pastry	6
Sandwiches, scones	2
Enriched bread, soft rolls	4
Dairy produce	
Cream	3
Eggs, unsalted butter	6
Hard cheese	3
Cream cheese	6

- Polythene boxes with airtight lids are also useful for freezing liquids, puréed fruit, cakes, etc. Boxes made especially for the freezer are stronger than other cheaper types.
- Foil cases are useful for casseroles, pies and flans. They are available in a variety of shapes and sizes; lids are often supplied, otherwise aluminium foil should be used to cover the food. Cases can be placed straight in the oven (cardboard lids should be removed first).
- Aluminium foil can be used to wrap food for freezing.
- Improvised containers, e.g. yoghurt and margarine cartons, can be used to freeze liquids, fruit purées, etc. Wash all containers thoroughly – do not use cracked ones.

Bags, foil cases and improvised containers should not be used to freeze food twice. Bags can be reused as a second covering, if they are first washed and dried.

Glass and china containers are unsuitable for long-term freezer storage as they cannot withstand very low temperatures.

Freezer organisation

The contents of the freezer should all be labelled with the name of the food and the date when frozen.

Foods should always be used in strict rotation; if the same types of food are grouped together in the freezer they can be identified easily. Smaller items can be stored in ice-cream containers for example, so they can be found easily.

Thawing

Generally most cooked foods are best thawed just before reheating, although some cooked foods can be heated from the frozen state; this will require a longer cooking time and therefore more fuel. A microwave oven can be used for thawing food (see Ch. 10).

Vegetables, especially those commercially frozen, should not be thawed prior to cooking. Meat can be cooked from frozen but extra cooking time should be allowed, and it is advisable to have a meat thermometer to check that the centre of the joint is properly cooked. Raw poultry *should always* be completely thawed prior to cooking, to ensure that the centre is cooked and that harmful food-poisoning bacteria are destroyed.

The best place to thaw food is either a refrigerator overnight or in a microwave oven. Bread can be thawed in a conventional oven at a low temperature; sliced bread can be toasted from frozen.

Chemical preservation

Food can be preserved by the addition of chemicals, e.g. sugar, salt and vinegar. Sugar and salt preserve food by dissolving in the water and making it unavailable for microbial growth; vinegar acidifies food so that micro-organisms are unable to survive.

At home, fruit and vegetables can be preserved by the addition of sugar to fruit to make jam. Vegetables can be preserved by pickling them in salt and vinegar.

Jam making

A good home-made jam tastes far fruitier than most bought varieties and can be made to preserve surplus home-grown fruit or when fruit is in season and cheap to buy.

The two main ingredients are fruit and sugar. When these ingredients are boiled together, a gel forms. In order to get a good set, it is important that the fruit contains the right amounts of pectin and acid. Pectin has different chemical forms – these change as the fruit ripens. The best gelling pectin is found in just ripe or slightly under-ripe fruit. Ripe fruit or very under-ripe fruit will not form a good jam. The fruit should also contain the right amount of acid which aids gel formation in pectin and also adds to the flavour. The amount of pectin and acid in fruit varies and this affects the setting of the jam.

The pectin and acid content of fruit is shown in Table 8.3.

TABLE 8.3 The pectin and acid content of fruit

High pectin/high acid fruit (sets easily)	Apples, bitter oranges, gooseberries, plums, damsons, lemons, black- and redcurrants
Moderate pectin/moderate acid fruit	Apricots, blackberries, raspberries
Low pectin/low acid fruit (do not set well)*	Cherries, pears, rhubarb, strawberries

* Lemon juice and commercial pectin can be added to low pectin/low acid fruits to get a good set.

Preserving sugar is available for jam making but granulated sugar is cheaper and will still give good results. The correct weight of sugar should be used in all recipes as too little will stop the jam setting properly, while too much will cause crystallisation of the jam on storage. Warm the sugar in a bowl in a pre-heated oven before adding to the fruit.

METHOD:
1. Prepare jam jars by cleaning thoroughly in warm soapy water. Rinse well and allow to drain. Dry the outsides with a tea towel and the insides by standing in an oven on a low light.
2. Cook the fruit in water, if necessary, until completely soft. Use a preserving pan or a large, thick-based pan. The process can be speeded up in fruit needing a long cooking time by using a pressure cooker.
3. Add the sugar and dissolve thoroughly.
4. Boil vigorously until setting point is reached; this usually takes 15–20 minutes. Setting point can be tested by several methods:
   (a) *Temperature* – when the jam reaches 105 °C/221 °F it is at

setting point. This can be measured by using a sugar thermometer.

(b) *Wrinkle test* – chill a small plate or saucer in the fridge. When the jam may have reached setting point, remove the plate from fridge and put a small teaspoon of jam on to the plate, allow to cool. Push jam with the finger, if it wrinkles, it has reached setting point.

(c) *Flake test* – remove a little jam from the pan with a clean, dry, wooden spoon. Cool slightly; tip the spoon; if the jam falls off in wide flakes it is ready; if it pours off the spoon in a trickle it needs further boiling.

While boiling the sugar and jam it is usual for a scum to develop; this is harmless but will spoil the finished jam. Remove with a metal spoon. A knob of butter or margarine added when the jam has reached setting point will also disperse the scum.

5. Pour jam into jars, while the jam is hot. Strawberry jam and marmalade are left in the pan for 15 minutes so that the fruit does not rise to the top. Use a heat-proof measuring jug to do this, filling the jars to the top. Cover with waxed discs and cover with dampened cellophane covers, secure with elastic, or use screw-top lids. Wipe jars with a hot damp cloth to remove any drips. Label when the jars are cold.

6. Store in a cool, dry and dark place.

7. If the jam has not set when cooled, pour back into the pan and reboil, adding the juice of a small lemon. If the jam develops mould it is preferable not to keep it.

Recipes

Strawberry jam – yield 2.75 kg (6 lb)
2 kg (4 lb) strawberries
1.35 kg (3 lb) sugar
4 tablespoons lemon juice

METHOD:
1. Hull and wash the strawberries, drain well. Layer with the sugar in a preserving pan and leave overnight.
2. To make the jam, dissolve the sugar fully over a low heat, add lemon juice and boil until setting point is reached; about 8–10 minutes.
3. Test for setting, following the general method of jam making from point 4.

Plum jam – yield 2.5 kg (5 lb)
1.5 kg (3 lb) plums
300 ml (½ pt) water
1.5 kg (3 lb) sugar

METHOD:
1. Wash the plums, cut in half and remove the stones. Wrap about ten stones in muslin, tie with string.
2. Simmer fruit in water until soft, with the stones.
3. Add sugar to pan, follow general method of jam making from point 4.

Marmalade – yield 2.75 kg (6 lb)
900 g (2 lb) Seville oranges
1 lemon
2.25 litres (4 pt) water
1.8 kg (4 lb) granulated sugar

METHOD:
1. Wash and scrub the oranges. Cut in half and squeeze out the juice. Squeeze the juice out of the lemon.
2. Tie all the pips in muslin, slice the orange peel very finely.
3. Put the orange peel, juice, pips and water into a large pan, bring to the boil and simmer for 1½–2 hours (or pressure cook for 20 minutes at 15 lb pressure, and allow to return to normal pressure at room temperature).
4. Discard bag and pips.
5. Add sugar, continue with general method from point 3.

Pickling
Vegetables are the main food item pickled, although fruit and hard-boiled eggs can be preserved by this method.

The addition of vinegar to vegetables preserves them because the acid in the vinegar prevents microbial growth. The vinegar used in pickling should contain at least 5 per cent acetic acid. White vinegar shows off the colour and texture of the pickles, but malt (brown) vinegar gives a better flavour. Spices are added to the vinegar to add to the flavour. Pickling spices can be purchased and added to vinegar. These should be added and left to infuse for 1–2 months. For a quicker method the spices can be boiled with the vinegar for 2 hours. Strain before use.

Alternatively, spiced vinegar can be purchased.

METHOD:

1. Vegetables should be sprinkled with salt to draw out any excess liquid. Layer the vegetables with salt and leave for 24–48 hours. Rinse in cold water and drain thoroughly.
2. Pack the vegetables in clean dry jars to 2.5 cm (1 in.) of the top.
3. Pour vinegar into jar to cover the vegetables. Allow any air bubbles to rise to the top.
4. Seal jars tightly; do not use metal lids as these will corrode with the vinegar.
5. Label and date the jars; store in a cool dry place for at least 2 months to allow the flavour to develop.

   Vegetables suitable: onions; cucumber; cauliflower.

QUESTIONS

1. What are the main points to remember when buying and storing food?
2. Prepare a poster showing personal hygiene rules for children who cook in schools.
3. What are the main differences between preserving food by reducing the temperature and using chemicals?

9

MEAL PLANNING AND ORGANISATION

Previous chapters dealt with the constituents of a healthy diet for the population, including special groups, e.g. children and expectant mothers. We must now apply this knowledge practically in the planning and organisation of meals.

When planning meals the following points should be considered:
1. The nutritional value of the meal and the nutritional requirements of the individuals who will be eating it.
2. The occasion for which the meal is required, and the appeal of the dishes to be served.
3. The season of the year and the weather.
4. The cooking ability of the cook, the facilities and equipment available.
5. The time available for preparation and cooking.
6. The amount of money to spend on the meal.

NUTRITIONAL CONTENT OF THE MEAL

The nutritional value of the meal and the requirements of those who will be eating it is important. Remember to include food from the five main food groups in the whole meal and to
• use wholemeal products to increase fibre;
• use as little fat as possible, particularly animal fat;
• use as little sugar as possible;
• reduce the amount of salt used in cooking.

The choice of dishes will depend on the requirements of the people who will eat the food; for example, you may be cooking for a group which includes a lacto-vegetarian and a person on a weight-reducing diet. In this case a meat- and fish-free main course would be chosen and the whole meal would be low in fat and sugar to reduce the energy content for the slimmer. The rest of the group could eat more unrefined carbohydrate as a filler, e.g. extra potatoes or wholemeal bread or serve wholemeal shortbread biscuits with an unsweetened fresh fruit salad.

ATTRACTIVENESS OF THE MEAL

Ordinary meals as well as meals for special occasions should have a variety of colours, textures and flavours to make them attractive.

The colour of a meal is very important, especially to children and to individuals who may have lost their appetites.

- Include different coloured vegetables, e.g. carrots and green beans, tomatoes and sweet corn or a mixed salad for main courses, especially if serving foods of a similar colour, e.g. fish and mashed potatoes.
- Do not serve similar foods in the same meal, e.g. oxtail soup and a beef casserole, or two pastry dishes, e.g. savoury flan and apple pie.
- Make sure that the courses in the meal compliment each other – for example, if you are cooking a heavy main course then choose a light pudding and vice versa.
- Provide different textures of foods, e.g. some soft, some crisp, some cooked, some raw.

SEASON AND WEATHER

Use fresh fruit and vegetables that are in season as they are usually cheaper to buy.

The dishes chosen should also compliment the season and weather; a hot meal will be appreciated on a cold winter's day but would probably be wasted in high summer.

FACILITIES AND EQUIPMENT AVAILABLE

Do not attempt very elaborate dishes if you are inexperienced, especially if you are preparing a meal for a special occasion.

When choosing to prepare and serve a particular dish, check that all the equipment is available for use.

FUEL ECONOMY

Fuel can be saved when cooking meals by:
- Cooking the whole meal in the oven, e.g. beef and vegetable casserole, jacket potatoes, baked apples with sultanas.
- Using all the oven to cook dishes for several meals, e.g. casseroles

for the next meal, and also dishes for freezing, e.g. puddings, flans, cakes.
- Using only the hot plates – a three-tier steamer to cook the whole meal or using a pressure cooker.
- When using hot plates save fuel by not turning the gas or electricity higher than necessary, and turning it off as soon as it is no longer required.

TIME AVAILABLE

The time available for cooking and preparing food should be considered when choosing a menu, as well as having every item ready to serve at the same time, but not over-cooked. This requires organisation. When the menu has been planned it is a good idea to make a chart of the preparation time, cooking time and any special points before working out a time plan.

For example, a meal may be:

    Tomato soup

    Chicken and vegetable casserole

    Jacket potatoes

    Fresh fruit salad and shortbread biscuits (made with wholemeal flour)

First of all, prepare a table to show cooking and preparation times and order of work (see Tables 9.1 and 9.2).

TABLE 9.1

Dish	Preparation time (mins)	Cooking time (mins)	Oven temperature/ shelf
Tomato soup	15	25	
Chicken and vegetable casserole	25	60	190 °C/Gas Mark 5
Jacket potatoes	5	60	200°C/Gas Mark 6
Fresh fruit salad	30		
Shortbread biscuits	15	15–20	170 °C/Gas Mark 3 Middle

Time plans can also be made when organising baking sessions (See Tables 9.3 and 9.4). It saves fuel to make several items at once as the oven will be full. Baked items can be easily frozen, e.g. if you are preparing the following frozen items: wholemeal bread rolls; flapjacks; savoury flan; fairy cakes.

TABLE 9.2

Time	Order or work
11.00	Light oven 170 °C/Gas Mark 3. Collect equipment and ingredients
11.05	Make shortbread biscuits
11.20	Shortbread biscuits to cook, wash up
11.25	Prepare chicken casserole
11.40	Take shortbread out of the oven. Turn oven up to 200 °C/Gas Mark 6
11.50	Chicken casserole in oven, bottom shelf. Wash up
11.55	Scrub potatoes
12.00	Potatoes to cook, top shelf. Prepare tomato soup
12.15	Soup to simmer. Prepare fresh fruit salad
12.40	Remove soup from heat, finish fresh fruit salad
12.45	Wash up
12.50	Liquidise and sieve soup, reheat
1.00	Serve meal

TABLE 9.3

Dish	Preparation time (mins)	Cooking time (mins)	Oven temperature/ shelf
Bread rolls	20	15–20	230 °C/Gas Mark 8
Flapjacks	15	15–20	190 °C/Gas Mark 5
Savoury flan	30	30–40	190 °C/Gas Mark 5
Fairy cakes	15	15	200 °C/Gas Mark 6

TABLE 9.4

Time	Order or work
2.00	Oven on 190 °C/Gas Mark 5. Collect equipment and ingredients
2.05	Prepare shortcrust pastry and flan ingredients
2.35	Flan to cook, wash up
2.40	Make flapjacks
2.55	Flapjacks to cook. Make bread rolls
3.15	Flan and flapjacks out of the oven, turn oven up to 200 °C/Gas Mark 6. Leave bread to prove
3.20	Prepare fairy cakes
3.35	Fairy cakes in oven
3.50	Fairy cakes out of the oven. Turn oven up to 230 °C/Gas Mark 8. Bread rolls to top of oven, wash up
4.10	Bread out of the oven
4.15	Decorate fairy cakes
4.25	Clear away

BUDGETING

Often only a certain amount of money is available to buy food. If this is the case it is important that the money is not squandered on expensive food items that are not good value nutritionally.

• Study the cost of the main items of the diet and look for special offers.
• Plan meals for a few days in advance and prepare a shopping list of the items you will require.
• Buy in large quantities if able – larger packets of dry goods and frozen foods are generally cheaper.
• Select cheaper protein foods, e.g. pulses, cheese, eggs rather than meat.
• Select cheaper cuts of meat, e.g. stewing meat, mince, liver and offal. Do not buy expensive convenience foods, e.g. meat pies, etc.

TABLE 9.5 Quantities of foods needed for children and adults (approximately)

Food	Children	Adults
Meat		
Chops	One (small)	One
Stewing meat	50 g	100 g
Roast meat	50 g	100 g
Meat with bone	75 g	150 g
Sausages/beefburgers	50 g	100 g
Cold meat	25–50 g	75–100 g
Fish		
Fillets	75 g	100 g
Whole fish, e.g. mackerel	½	One
Cheese	25 g	50 g
Pulses	50 g	100–150 g
Vegetables		
Potatoes	50–100 g	200 g
Green vegetables	50 g	100–150 g
Carrots and other roots	50 g	100 g
Tomatoes	50 g	50–75 g
Fruit		
Stewing fruit	50 g	100 g
Soup	125 ml	125–250 ml
Milk puddings	70 g	175 g
Custards	50 ml	125 ml
Sauces and gravies	30 ml	60 ml

- Calculate the quantities of food required, especially fresh foods, to avoid buying too much which is wasted (see Table 9.5).

QUESTIONS

1. Plan a nutritionally well-balanced meal for the following family: mother; father (on a weight-reducing diet because of heart disease); teenage son (will not eat meat or fish); and 8-year-old child.
2. Make a time plan for the meal you choose to prepare.
3. Write down all the food you have to eat in one day – find out how much it cost.

10

METHODS OF COOKING

Most of the foods that we eat are cooked in some way; food is cooked to make it easier to digest and to kill any harmful bacteria. Foods often look and taste more pleasant when cooked and can be more appetising. There are four main methods of cooking food. These are:
• moist methods – liquid is used to apply heat;
• dry methods – heat is directly applied;
• frying methods – fats or oils are used to apply heat;
• microwaving – heat is generated by electromagnetic waves.
   The choice of method used depends on the food to be cooked, the time available and individual preference.
   When cooking food it is important to try and retain as many nutrients in the food as possible, this is especially important when cooking foods such as vegetables.

MOIST METHODS OF COOKING

These methods use a liquid to cook food – this may be water, stock, steam, milk or fruit juice. Methods include boiling, poaching, stewing, steaming and pressure cooking.
   Water-soluble nutrients may be lost into the liquid when cooking by moist methods, especially vitamin C, folic acid and thiamin. It is a good idea to use the liquid to make sauces or gravies. Moist methods usually use low temperatures.
   Pressure cookery retains nutrients as the food is cooked very quickly at high pressure.

BOILING

This is the most widely used method of cooking foods such as vegetables, eggs, rice and pasta. The food is cooked in just enough boiling liquid to cover the food. For cooking rice and pasta the water should be bubbling evenly and rapidly; this prevents the food from sticking at the bottom of the pan. Vegetables, especially potatoes, would soon break up if they were subjected to such harsh treatment; 'boiled' vegetables are, in fact, 'simmered'.

Simmering is a gentler treatment where the liquid is just below boiling point with occasional bubbles rising to the surface. The cooking liquid from vegetables should be used to make gravy or sauce to serve with the meal.

POACHING

Poaching is a gentler form of simmering where the liquid, usually water or milk, only half covers the food. It is used mainly to cook fish or eggs.

STEAMING

Steaming involves cooking food in steam rising from boiling water. The food is not in contact with the liquid. This method is used to cook foods such as fish, meat and sponge puddings and vegetables. Steamed food is often soft and light and can be used for invalids. Serve crisp food in a meal containing steamed dishes to add to the texture.

Vegetables take a long time to cook if steamed, therefore losses of vitamin C can be great.

Methods of steaming
• Universal or graduated steamer – this is made to fit over most saucepans and has holes in the base to allow steam to pass through. Food to be steamed is placed in a covered basin or wrapped in foil (see Fig. 10.1).

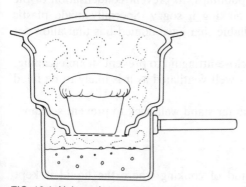

FIG. 10.1 Universal steamer

- Food, especially fish, can be cooked on a plate over a pan of boiling water. The pan lid is placed over the plate. Potatoes can be cooked in the water at the same time (see Fig. 10.2).
- Meat and sponge puddings can be steamed in a covered basin inside a pan of boiling water. Place the basin on a trivet to make sure the bottom does not burn (see Fig. 10.3).

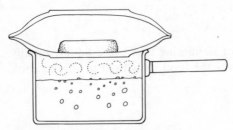

FIG. 10.2 Steaming between two plates

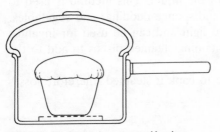

FIG. 10.3 Steaming in a covered basin

Points to remember
1. The water should be boiling constantly while the food is cooking.
2. Keep a kettle of boiling water at hand to replenish the steamer.
3. Cover food, especially puddings, to prevent condensation of the steam on to the food making it soggy. Specially made plastic pudding basins are available that have domed lids that allow for rising.
4. Make sure pans have a close-fitting lid to prevent steam escaping; make sure the kitchen is well ventilated as it is likely to be filled with moisture.
5. When dismantling a steamer stand well back to prevent scalding.

STEWING

This is a slow moist method of cooking where the liquid is kept below boiling point. It is used to cook vegetables and meat,

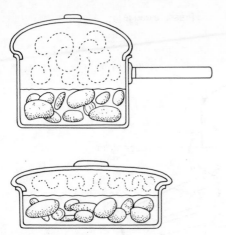

FIG. 10.4 Stewing in a pan or casserole

particularly the tough cheaper cuts which can become very tender and appetising if stewed. Normally the cooking liquid is served with the food. Stewing can be carried out either on top of the cooker in a pan with a tight-fitting lid or in a casserole dish in the oven (see Fig. 10.4).

This is an easy method of cooking as stews are easy to prepare and the food 'looks after itself' once cooking. The whole of the main course can be cooked by this method and can be prepared in advance, using an automatic oven timer to start the cooking. A variety of stews can be prepared although the texture does tend to be soft; therefore crisp vegetables or other courses should be included with a stew.

Slow cookers are ideal for stewing, although pulse vegetables may not be cooked thoroughly enough to destroy toxins present, particularly in red kidney beans (see Ch. 11).

PRESSURE COOKERY

Normally water boils at 100 °C; this is at atmospheric pressure and will not increase, even if boiling continues for a long period. However, if the pressure is increased, the temperature at which water boils will also increase. This means that food will be cooked faster because the temperature of the food is higher, which not only retains more nutrients but also saves fuel.

Pressure cookers are thicker than ordinary saucepans and are made from aluminium or stainless steel. A typical pressure cooker is shown in Fig. 10.5.

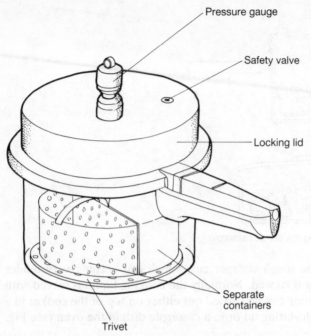

FIG. 10.5 A typical pressure cooker

The pressure gauge is fitted over the control valve. In some models the gauge has a central pin which rises as pressure builds up and indicates the pressure by a series of marks or the gauge may contain separate weights.

Recipes indicate the pressure required, e.g.:

Low   (0.35 kg/sq. cm (5 lb/sq. in.)) = 107 °C
Medium   (0.7 kg/sq. cm (10 lb/sq. in.)) = 112 °C
High   (1.05 kg/sq. cm (15 lb/sq. in.)) = 120 °C

The control valve allows a small amount of steam to escape to control the build-up of pressure. If the pressure inside the cooker becomes too great, it will be released through the *safety valve* which will either melt or be pushed out.

The lid always locks and the *gasket* (or rubber seal) inside the lock ensures that the pressure cooker is steamtight.

The *trivet* enables food to be cooked above the minimum of liquid necessary (300 ml). *Separators* allow different types of food to be cooked at the same time.

Points to remember

1. A minimum of 300 ml (½ pt) of liquid should be used to ensure adequate build-up of steam.

2. The cooker should never be more than two-thirds full of solid food or half-full with liquids. Greater quantities may block the control valve.

3. The lid should be locked in position and the cooker heated so that steam escapes *before* the pressure gauge is positioned. This ensures that all air in the cooker is expelled. Air left inside the cooker can cause discolouration of vegetables and will affect the cooking temperature.

4. A steady hissing sound indicates that the pressure has built up to the desired level. Lower the heat to maintain the pressure and start the cooking time.

5. When the cooking time is completed, turn off the head and reduce the pressure inside the cooker either by leaving at room temperature or pouring a gentle stream of cold water over the cooker. Do not attempt to remove the lid until the pressure has reduced to normal.

Most manufacturers of pressure cookers supply a recipe leaflet to indicate the pressure and cooking times for dishes. These and other instructions should be followed carefully.

Foods suitable for pressure cooking include meat and meat dishes, vegetables – not frozen as these cook as fast at normal pressure – but particularly pulse vegetables which require long cooking times, puddings, soups, jam making.

DRY METHODS OF COOKING

Roasting, baking and grilling are dry methods of cooking where the heat is applied directly to the food. High temperatures are used in dry methods which have different effects on the food than in moist methods of cooking. Roasting and baking are carried out in a conventional oven.

ROASTING AND BAKING

In both these methods the food browns, giving an attractive appearance, e.g. the colour of bread, biscuits and roast meats. Baking is the term used to describe the cooking of flour mixtures, e.g. cakes, bread, biscuits, pastry in an oven. Other foods are also baked, e.g. fruit (baked apples) and potatoes. True roasting is carried out on a rotating spit over a fierce heat, but today any food that is basted with fat in the oven is 'roasted'. It is generally confined to the cooking of meat and vegetables, especially potatoes. In order to

TABLE 10.1 Roasting times

Suitable cuts	Cooking time (on the bone)	Temperature	Accompaniments
Beef Sirloin Rib Silverside	20 mins per 450 g + 20 mins (25 + 25 for boned)	220 °C/ Gas Mark 7	Yorkshire pudding, horseradish sauce
Lamp Leg Shoulder	20 mins per 450 g + 20 mins	220 °C/ Gas Mark 7	Mint sauce, redcurrant jelly
Pork Leg Loin Spare rib	35 mins per 450 g + 35 mins	190 °C/ Gas Mark 5	Apple sauce, sage and onion stuffing
Chicken	20 mins per 450 g + 20 mins	200 °C/ Gas Mark 6	Bread sauce, bacon rolls, stuffing, chipolata sausages

reduce the fat content of roast meat, it can be wrapped in foil which helps prevent shrinkage. It is preferable to roast vegetables in oil rather than lard or dripping to reduce the saturated fat intake (see Ch. 3).

Tough cuts of beef do not roast well as moist methods are needed to make the meat tender.

Sirloin, topside and ribs are cuts of beef that are suitable for roasting.

All large cuts of pork and lamb and poultry can be roasted.

Table 10.1 shows the roasting times for meat.

GRILLING

This is another dry method of cooking. The temperatures are very high and the food is in very close contact with the source of heat; therefore the food is cooked quickly. Only tender cuts of meat can be cooked by this method because of the short cooking time. Foods should not be more than 2.5–3.5 cm (1–1.5 in.) thick to allow the heat to penetrate to cook the centre of the food. The food should be turned frequently to ensure even cooking.

Foods suitable include: chops, steaks, bacon, liver, chicken joints, sausages, fish, beefburgers, tomatoes, mushrooms.

Grilling can be used to brown foods, e.g. cheese, macaroni cheese sauces, and to toast bread. Grilling is a very healthy way of cooking food as the fat from the meat drains away and is not eaten.

FRYING

Frying is a quick method of cooking in fat or oil. When food is fried the fat used in cooking is absorbed into the food, thus increasing the fat and energy content of the food. As it is advisable to reduce the amount of fat, particularly animal fat in the diet, fried foods should not be eaten regularly and, if frying is used as a method of cooking, a vegetable oil is preferable or a non-stick pan should be used which needs very little or no fat.

There are two types of frying, either shallow or deep frying.

SHALLOW FRYING

Some foods do not need any oil when frying, e.g. bacon and sausages, since there is enough fat in these foods to prevent them from sticking. When frying other foods a little oil is required to cover the bottom of the frying pan to prevent sticking. Most foods that are shallow fried can also be grilled (except for eggs) and this is a healthier way of cooking.

DEEP FRYING

Food that is deep fried is completely immersed in hot oil. A strong deep pan or chip pan should be used with a frying basket. Most foods, other than potatoes, are too fragile to withstand hot oil without breaking and need a coating for protection, e.g. flour and beaten egg, egg and breadcrumbs or oatmeal or batter. These are used for fish.

Vegetable oil is the best type of fat to be used in frying for health reasons. The oil should be clear and fresh. Oil that contains water or impurities affects the flavour and keeping qualities of the oil. The oil should not be heated beyond the required temperature as it can burst into flames.

Safety
- Never fill the pan more than two-thirds full.
- Lower the food into the oil gently.
- When deep frying watch the food *constantly*. Many fires in the home start from an unattended chip pan which catches fire.
- *Always* make sure that the pan is beyond the reach of children.
- If a pan catches fire, cover it with the lid, thick towel or a baking sheet. Turn the heat off. Do not throw water on to the pan and *never* try to move the pan until the oil has cooled down.

MICROWAVE COOKERY

Microwave ovens can be used for cooking, defrosting and reheating food. The advantages of using a microwave are that food can be cooked far faster than using a conventional oven and the food can be cooked on serving dishes, therefore cutting down on washing up. These advantages make microwaves very convenient, especially if families cannot eat together at the same time; food can be prepared and reheated very quickly when required. For people living alone they are particularly convenient as nutritious meals can be prepared and cooked very quickly without having to dirty a lot of pans.

Because food cooks faster in a microwave it is cheaper, especially if a conventional electric cooker has been used. Not all foods can be microwaved successfully. Foods do not become crisp and may not develop colours and textures of conventionally cooked versions. It is impossible to deep fry in a microwave, boil eggs in their shells or to make Yorkshire pudding, meringues or choux pastry. This is because microwaves cook from the inside and so it is impossible to achieve a soft interior and crisp crust needed for these recipes. Meringue toppings, e.g. on lemon meringue pies, which can be crunchy throughout can be cooked very successfully in a microwave oven. As food is cooked quickly, nutrient losses are low.

HOW DO MICROWAVE OVENS WORK?

Microwaves are electromagnetic waves. They move at the speed of light and have a very high frequency (i.e. they vibrate millions of times per second). If absorbed into a food, the vibrations of the microwave agitate the molecules in the food, causing a rise in temperature. Microwaves can penetrate up to 5 cm (2 in.) into food and produce heat rapidly from the inside. They are produced by a valve in the oven called a magnetron.

Foods that are thicker than 5 cm (2 in.) can still be cooked in a microwave as the heat will move into the centre of the food by conduction. Microwaves do not remain in the food so that it is safe to eat.

Some materials do not absorb microwaves but *transmit* them, i.e. they allow microwaves to pass through them but they do not heat up. Such materials are paper, china and some plastics. These materials can be used as containers; they do not heat up due to the microwaves but will become warm because of conduction of heat from the cooked foods.

Microwaves can be *reflected* from some materials, e.g. metals.

The metals do not heat up and will reflect microwaves back to the magnetron causing permanent damage to the oven.

Microwave ovens do not heat up like conventional ovens. There is always a safety device on the door of microwave cookers to ensure that microwaves are not emitted once the door is opened.

The instruction booklet accompanying individual ovens should be carefully studied before using a microwave oven.

QUESTIONS

1. Describe the effect of all methods of cooking on the nutrient content of food.
2. What are the three main methods of steaming?
3. What is the difference between stewing and roasting meats? Which cuts are most suitable for both methods?
4. How do pressure cookers and microwave ovens cook food?
5. What are the safety precautions necessary when deep frying?

11

RECIPES

NOTES ON RECIPES

1. Use metric or imperial weights only in the recipes; do not use a combination of the two.
2. Use wholemeal flour totally or partially in the recipes to increase the fibre content of the dish.
3. Use a polyunsaturated margarine in recipes, or vegetable oil.
4. Where the recipe includes stock cubes, no extra salt should be necessary.

STARTERS AND SOUPS

Starters and soups can be served as the first course of a meal or as the main course of a light meal, e.g. pâté and wholemeal bread or lentil soup and bread rolls.

The first course of a meal should encourage the appetite and should contrast with the main course. Portions should be fairly small – you need to leave enough room for the main course and dessert!

Tomato or fruit juice or fresh fruit such as melon or grapefruit are refreshing and easily prepared starters.

Homemade soups are more economical and far more flavoursome than tinned, dehydrated or instant soups. They are relatively simple to prepare, especially if a liquidiser or food processor and pressure cooker are available.

COLD STARTERS

Grapefruit (per person)
½ grapefruit
1 glacé cherry

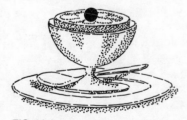

FIG. 11.1

METHOD:
1. Cut each grapefruit in half. Using a grapefruit knife, loosen the flesh from the outer skin of each half, then cut between the segments to loosen the flesh from the membranes.
2. Chill. Just before serving decorate with a glacé cherry. Serve with castor sugar if desired (see Fig. 11.1).

Sliced melon

FIG. 11.2

METHOD:
1. Cut the melon into wedge-shaped slices, remove the seeds from the centre.
2. With a sharp knife loosen the flesh from the skin. Cut the flesh at right angles to form wedge-shaped pieces.
3. Decorate with a slice of orange and a cherry, serve at room temperature. Ground ginger mixed with castor sugar can be sprinkled on the melon (see Fig. 11.2).

Florida cocktail (serves 4)
2 oranges
2 grapefruit
4 glacé cherries

METHOD:
1. Cut the top and bottom layer of skin off a grapefruit and remove the skin with a sharp knife, to reveal all the pulp.
2. Hold the fruit in one hand and carefully remove all the segments from the dividing membranes. Work over a bowl to collect the juice.
3. Repeat (1) and (2) for the other grapefruit and the oranges.
4. Mix the segments and juice together, chill.
5. Serve in glass dishes, decorated with a glacé cherry.

Smoked mackerel pâté (serves 4)

2 smoked mackerel fillets   juice of ½ a lemon
75 ml (3 oz) natural yoghurt   salt, pepper
50 g (2 oz) cottage cheese

METHOD:
1. Scrape the flesh from the mackerel fillet skins, remove any bones. Flake the skin.
2. Liquidise the fish, yoghurt, cottage cheese and lemon juice until smooth.
3. Season to taste.
4. Spoon into individual bowls, cover with cling film and chill for several hours.
5. Just before serving, garnish with cress and lemon wedges. Serve with wholemeal toast.

Avocado pears with curd cheese (per person)

½ avocado pear   1 lettuce leaf
25 g (1 oz) curd cheese   freshly chopped chives

METHOD:
1. Split ripe avocados in half lengthwise, remove the stone.
2. Spoon the curd cheese into the hollow left by the stone.
3. Place on a lettuce leaf on a dessert plate, garnish with chives.

Variation: prawns can be added instead of the curd cheese, omit the chives but add French dressing (see p. 137).

SOUPS

Lentil soup (serves 4)

100 g (4 oz) potato   1 chicken stock cube
100 g (4 oz) onion   750 ml (1½ pt) water
2 sticks of celery   salt, pepper, pinch mixed herbs
100 g (4 oz) red split lentils   150 ml (6 oz) milk

METHOD:
1. Peel the potato and onion, slice the onion and dice the potato and celery.
2. Wash the lentils in a sieve, drain.
3. Put all the ingredients except the milk in a pan, bring to the boil, stirring. Reduce the heat and cover.

4. Simmer for 1 hour (or pressure cook at H/15 lb pressure for 15 minutes).
5. Liquidise or sieve, return to the pan, add the milk and reheat. Check the seasoning, serve.

Celery soup (serves 4)

1 head of celery	salt and pepper, pinch of mixed
100 g (4 oz) onion	herbs
1 chicken stock cube	25 g (1 oz) flour
750 ml (1½ pt) water	150 ml (6 oz) milk

METHOD:
1. Wash and dice the celery, slice the onion.
2. Put all the ingredients, except for the flour and milk, in a pan, bring to the boil, reduce the heat and cover.
3. Simmer for about 40 minutes. Liquidise and sieve.
4. Blend the flour with a little of the milk, gently reheat the soup with the rest of the milk, add the blended flour, stirring constantly.
5. Heat gently for 5 minutes to cook the flour, check the seasoning and serve.

French onion soup (serves 4)

750 g (1½ lb) onions	salt and pepper
50 g (2 oz) margarine	4 slices of French bread
1 litre (1¾ pt) water	50 g (2 oz) grated cheese
2 beef stock cubes	

FIG. 11.3

METHOD:
1. Peel the onions and chop roughly.
2. Melt the margarine in a large pan, fry the onions until golden brown.
3. Add the water, stock cubes, salt and pepper, bring to the boil,

reduce the heat and simmer for 25 minutes (or pressure cook for 3 minutes at H/15 lb pressure).
4. Put one slice of bread each into four soup plates. Pour the soup over the bread and sprinkle with grated cheese (see Fig. 11.3).

Other dishes suitable for starters: salads, slices of pizza, individual quiches.

FISH

Fish is available as fresh, frozen, smoked or tinned. On the whole we do not eat a lot of fish in this country, and when it is eaten it is usually frozen. As fish is a good source of protein but not of saturated fat it would be beneficial to eat more.

Fish cooks quickly but can lack colour and flavour. Serve it with a well-flavoured sauce, e.g. cheese or tomato, and use colourful garnishes, e.g. parsley, cress or lemon wedges.

There are three main types of fish: white, oily and shellfish.

WHITE FISH

The group contains all fish with white flesh, e.g. haddock, plaice, whiting and sole. White fish is a good source of protein. There is no fat in the flesh therefore the energy value of white fish is low (providing no fat is added during cooking). It is also easily digested. The liver of white fish contains vitamins A and D.

Some white fish is smoked, e.g. smoked haddock and cod, this adds flavour to the fish and it will also keep fresh longer.

OILY FISH

Oily fish have oil in their flesh and include herrings, mackerel, sardines, salmon and trout.

Oily fish are a good source of protein, polyunsaturated fats and vitamins A and D. Many varieties are canned, and if the fish are eaten whole, e.g. sardines, the bones provide a good source of calcium. Oily fish are also smoked, e.g. smoked mackerel, kippers (smoked herrings), smoked salmon and smoked trout.

SHELLFISH

Shellfish include lobster, crab, oysters, prawns, shrimps, cockles and mussels. They are protected by a shell, which has to be removed before eating. Shellfish are the most expensive types of fish. They are a good source of protein, and shrimps and prawns are also low in energy.

FRESH FISH

Fresh fish should be eaten within one day of purchase if kept in a refrigerator, on the day if kept in a cool place. When buying fresh fish the flesh should be firm and moist. Whole fish should have sparkling scales and bright prominent eyes. Stale fish looks dull and droopy and should not be purchased. A fishmonger will skin and fillet whole fish.

Fish cakes (makes 6)

100 g (4 oz) white fish or tuna fish
200 g (8 oz) cooked and mashed potatoes
15 g (½ oz) margarine

salt and pepper
1 level tablespoon freshly chopped parsley

FIG. 11.4

For the coating:
flour, 1 beaten egg, breadcrumbs, oil for frying

METHOD:
1. If using white fish, steam it between two plates (see p. 100).
2. Flake the fish, mix it with the potatoes, margarine, salt and pepper and the parsley.
3. Divide the mixture into six pieces, shape into round cakes, or for children into fish shapes. Coat each with flour, beaten egg and breadcrumbs.
4. Fry gently in oil, drain well on kitchen paper (see Fig. 11.4).

Fish with tomato sauce (serves 4)
4 white fish steaks, fresh or frozen
For the tomato sauce:
25 ml (1 oz) oil
500 g (1 lb) tomatoes, skinned and chopped
1 clove of garlic, crushed

1 tablespoon freshly chopped parsley
50 ml (2 oz) fish stock or water
salt and pepper

METHOD:
1. Skin the tomatoes by plunging into a bowl of hot water; this will ease the skin away from the flesh.
2. Heat the oil in a pan, add the tomatoes, garlic, stock, salt and pepper and simmer for 10 minutes, stirring occasionally.
3. Place the fish in a casserole dish, pour the sauce over the fish. Bake in an oven at 190 °C/Gas Mark 5 for 20 minutes.

Fried fish (serves 4)

4 fillets of white fish	fresh breadcrumbs
1 beaten egg	oil for frying
flour	

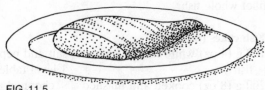

FIG. 11.5

METHOD:
1. Wash and dry the fish. Place the flour, beaten egg and bread-crumbs in separate dishes.
2. Dip the fish into the flour, then the egg, finally coating with the crumbs.
3. Heat the oil in a frying pan, fry the fish gently for about 8 minutes on each side.
4. When cooked, drain well on kitchen paper. Serve with a lemon wedge and a sprig of parsley (see Fig. 11.5).

Fish pie (serves 4)

400 g (1 lb) white fish	600 g (1½ lb) potatoes, cooked
200 g (8 oz) peas	and mashed
375 ml (¾ pt) milk	milk and margarine
40 g (1½ oz) flour	salt and pepper

METHOD:
1. Skin and wash the fish, simmer gently in a pan with the peas and milk for about 10 minutes.
2. Remove fish and peas from the pan, set on one side. Remove any bones from the fish, flake.
3. Blend the flour with a little water, add to the milk and heat gently until the sauce thickens. Add seasoning to taste.
4. Add the cooked fish and peas into the sauce, place in a casserole dish.

5. Add milk and margarine to the mashed potatoes and spread or pipe on top of the fish mixture.
6. Bake in a hot oven, 220 °C/Gas Mark 7 for 40 minutes or until the potatoes are light brown in colour. Garnish with tomato and parsley.

Fish pie can be made in individual dishes for children.

Fish recipes in other sections include: mackerel pâté (p. 110), tuna fish salad (p. 140).

MEAT

Meat includes all types of carcass meat from cows (beef), sheep (lamb), pigs (pork, bacon and ham), offal and poultry. Meat and meat products form the basis of the majority of people's daily meals in the UK.

NUTRITIONAL VALUE

Meat is a valuable source of protein in the diet. Some meat products have lower quantities of protein because they have been extended by cereals and often contain a lot of fat, e.g. sausages and beef-burgers. Red meat, i.e. beef and lamb, liver and kidney, are sources of haem iron, which is absorbed more efficiently than non-haem sources of iron. Meat is also a source of other minerals and B group vitamins.

Beef, lamb, pork, bacon and ham and products made from these meats all contain a lot of saturated fat. As it is beneficial to reduce this type of fat in the diet it would be better to eat less of these meats and more chicken and fish which have a lower fat content. All visible fat should be removed from these meats.

STORING MEAT

Always store meat in a cool place, preferably the refrigerator. Discard the wrapping paper and cover with cling film or foil on a plate to prevent loss of moisture. Raw meat will keep for 2–3 days, except for liver and minced meat which should be used within 1 day of purchase. Cooked meat will keep for up to 3 days.

Frozen meat should thaw at room temperature or in a microwave before cooking, and it is important to ensure complete thawing in joints of meat and poultry.

CUTS OF MEAT

Carcass meat is cut into different joints. The leaner and tender cuts are from the part of the animal that does little work, e.g. fillet, sirloin, topside and rump of beef, fillet of lamb and pork, chicken breasts. These are the most expensive types, whereas the cheaper joints are from the part of the animal that are involved with a great deal of movement. Examples include leg and neck joints. Breast of lamb and belly pork are also cheaper as they contain a lot of fat (see Fig. 11.6).

Cheaper cuts of meat contain as much protein as the more expensive varieties and can be made as appealing as tender cuts by careful preparation and cooking.

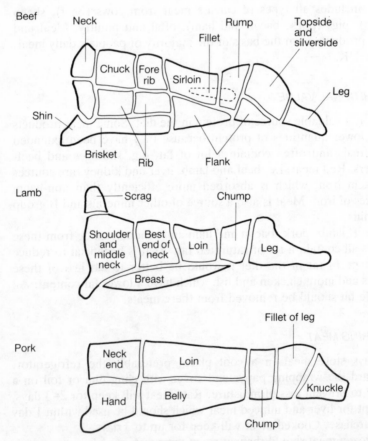

FIG. 11.6 Traditional cuts of meat (some butchers are adopting continental cuts as these are leaner and contain less fat)

OFFAL

This is the term for the internal organs of the animal and includes liver, kidney, tongue, heart, brain, sweetbread (pancreas) and tripe.

POULTRY

Poultry includes chicken, turkey, goose and duck. Chicken is a very popular meat and is fairly inexpensive. It is available fresh or frozen as a whole chicken or as joints. It is important that frozen chicken is thawed completely before cooking or the inside may not cook thoroughly. This could mean that harmful bacteria are not destroyed.

METHODS OF COOKING MEAT

Roasting: see Chapter 10 for details.
Stewing: cheaper cuts of all types of meat can be cooked in a stew
  or a casserole, including liver and sausages.
Grilling: the more tender cuts of meat can be grilled, e.g. rump and
  fillet steak, pork and lamb chops, bacon, ham, sausages, beefburgers and liver.

Grilling times
  Lamb chops   7–10 minutes on each side
  Pork chops   10–15 minutes on each side
  Steak   10–15 minutes on each side
  Gammon   10–15 minutes on each side

Beef or chicken casserole (serves 4)
400 g (1 lb) stewing beef or   1 large tin of tomatoes
  4 chicken joints   liquid from the tinned tomatoes
100 g (4 oz) carrot   plus water to make 500 ml (1 pt)
50 g (2 oz) celery   salt, pepper, pinch of mixed
100 g (4 oz) mushrooms   herbs cornflour
100 g (4 oz) onion   •   oil
1 green pepper
1 stock cube – beef or chicken

METHOD:
1. Peel and dice the onion, carrots and mushroom. Slice the green
   pepper and chop the celery.
2. Fry the meat in a little oil for about 5 minutes, stirring the beef

FIG. 11.7

constantly or turning the chicken. Remove from the pan then fry the onion, until soft.

3. Place the meat and onion in a casserole dish, add the chopped vegetables, and tinned tomatoes.
4. Add the liquid and the stock cube into the pan, bring to the boil. Stir in blended cornflour (the amount to use depends on the required thickness of the sauce). Season to taste with salt, pepper and mixed herbs.
5. Pour sauce over the meat and vegetables, cover and bake at 180 °C/Gas Mark 4 for 1¼–1½ hrs or until the meat is tender and the vegetables are soft. Serve with jacket potatoes, baked at the same time (see Fig. 11.7).

Moussaka (serves 4)

4 large aubergines
salt, oil
400 g (1 lb) minced lamb
200 g (8 oz) onion
25 g (1 oz) flour
1 clove garlic, crushed

1 large can of tomatoes
pinch mixed herbs
1 tablespoon freshly chopped parsley
250 ml (½ pt) cheese sauce (see p. 124)
50 g (2 oz) grated cheese
pepper

METHOD:

1. Slice the aubergines into rings, sprinkle with salt and leave for 30 minutes (this removes the bitter juices). Drain with kitchen paper.
2. Fry the slices in oil until brown on both sides, remove from the pan.
3. Brown the minced lamb in the remaining oil, add the chopped onion and cook for 10 minutes, stir in the crushed garlic.

4. Blend in the flour and tinned tomatoes (with juice). Season to taste with herbs, salt and pepper.
5. Arrange the aubergine slices and the meat mixture in alternate layers in a casserole dish, ending with a layer of aubergines.
6. Pour over the cheese sauce and sprinkle with the grated cheese.
7. Bake in a hot oven 200 °C/Gas Mark 6 for 1 hour. Serve with a green salad.

Pork chops with apricots (serves 4)

4 pork chops	2 tablespoons tomato purée
25 ml (1 oz) oil	1 crushed glove garlic
100 g (4 oz) onion	2 bay leaves
15 g (½ oz) flour	4 tablespoons vinegar
1 large can apricots (in fruit juice)	

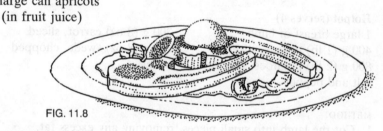

FIG. 11.8

METHOD:
1. Remove the fat from the chops, fry in oil, until browned. Place in a casserole dish.
2. Chop the onion and fry in the oil, stir in the flour and cook for several minutes. Add the juice from the apricots, tomato purée, garlic, bay leaves and vinegar. Season to taste. Bring to the boil, stirring constantly, for 1–2 minutes.
3. Arrange the apricots over the chops, reserving four for garnish.
4. Pour the sauce over the chops and apricots, cover and cook at 180 °C/Gas Mark 4 for 1 hour. Garnish with apricots and parsley (see Fig. 11.8).

Chicken and mushroom pie (serves 4)
200 g (8 oz) wholemeal shortcrust pastry (see p. 149)
Filling:

2 tablespoons oil	250 ml (½ pt) chicken stock
100 g (4 oz) onion, chopped	400 g (1 lb) cooked chicken, diced
1 crushed clove of garlic	
100 g (4 oz) mushrooms, sliced	1 tablespoon freshly chopped parsley
1 tablespoon flour	salt and pepper

METHOD:

1. Heat the oil in a pan, fry the onion until softened, add the garlic and mushrooms, cook for 5 minutes.
2. Stir in the blended flour and stock, bring to the boil and cook until thickened, stirring constantly.
3. Add water to come half-way up the casserole. Cook in an oven, pie dish.
4. Cover the pie with the rolled out pastry, firstly covering the rim of the pie dish with a narrow strip of pastry. Moisten the strip with water then cover with the pastry. Trim and press the edges down firmly. Make a hole in the centre of the pastry, to allow steam to escape.
5. Bake at 200 °C/Gas Mark 6 for 30 minutes.

Hotpot (serves 4)

1 large breast of lamb	200 g (8 oz) carrot, sliced
400 g (1 lb) onions, sliced	200 g (8 oz) swede, chopped
800 g (2 lb) potatoes, sliced	water
salt and pepper	

METHOD:

1. Cut the lamb into small pieces, removing any excess fat.
2. Layer the onion, potatoes, meat, carrot and swede in a large casserole dish, ending with a layer of potato. Season each layer.
3. Add water to come half-way up the casserole. Cook in a oven, covered, at 180 °C/Gas Mark 4 for 1 hour. Remove the cover and cook for a further hour.

Beefburgers (makes 4)

200 g (8 oz) minced beef
50 g (2 oz) onion, grated
salt and pepper
flour

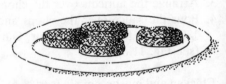

FIG. 11.9

METHOD:

1. Mix the minced beef, onion and salt and pepper together thoroughly.
2. Divide into four and shape into round cakes, no more than 20 mm/¾ in. thick on a floured board. Animal cutters could be used for children.
3. Grill on each side for 8 minutes (see Fig. 11.9).

Savoury minced beef (serves 4)

400 g (1 lb) minced beef	25 g (1 oz) flour
100 g (4 oz) onion, sliced	salt and pepper
250 ml (½ pt) beef stock	2 tablespoons tomato purée

METHOD:

1. Brown the minced beef in a pan, drain off any excess fat.
2. Add the onion, continue cooking until the onion is softened.
3. Pour the beef stock over the meat mixture, stir in the tomato purée. Add the blended flour, stirring well. Season to taste. Cook for a further 15 minutes.

Serve with vegetables and potatoes/rice or use to make:

Shepherds pie

1 quantity savoury minced beef
400 g (1 lb) mashed potatoes, mixed with margarine and milk

METHOD:

1. Place the minced beef in a pie dish.
2. Spread or pipe the mashed potatoes on top of the minced beef.
3. Bake at 200 °C/Gas Mark 6 for 30–40 minutes or until the potatoes are golden brown.

Minced beef pie

1 quantity savoury minced beef	150 g (6 oz) wholemeal
200 g (8 oz) carrot, grated	shortcrust
100 g (4 oz) peas	pastry or 100 g (4 oz) rough-puff pastry

METHOD:

1. Combine the minced beef with the carrots and peas. Pour into a pie dish.
2. Roll the pastry out, place narrow strips on the edge of the pie dish, moisten the edges and place the rolled out pastry over the top. Trim and seal the edges. Make a hole in the centre for steam to escape.
3. Bake at 200 °C/Gas Mark 6 for 20–30 minutes or until the pie is golden brown.

Meat recipes in other sections include: curry (p. 128), chilli con carne (p. 134), rissotto (p. 130), spaghetti bolognese (p. 131), lasagne (p. 131), spaghetti carbonara (p. 132), pasties (p. 151) and sausage rolls (p. 152).

CHEESE AND EGGS

Both cheese and eggs are very useful foods because they can be made into a variety of quick snacks and can form an economical replacement for meat and fish in main meals. Cheese and eggs contain protein of high biological value. Hard cheese and eggs do contain a high proportion of saturated animal fats, therefore their consumption should be limited.

CHEESE

Most of the cheese consumed in the UK is made from cow's milk although many continental cheeses that are available are made from goat's and ewe's milk. Cheese is made by coagulating the milk protein 'casein' to form 'curds'. Usually a starter is added, normally rennet, to speed up the coagulation process. The curds are drained to remove most of the liquid or 'whey', and salt is added. The cheese is then pressed and left to mature; this develops the flavour and texture.

Types of cheese
Many different types of cheeses are available throughout the world. The variations are due to the different types of milk used and varying methods of production. Many traditional cheeses have other ingredients added to them, e.g. sage in Sage Derby, peppers in Brie, chutney in Double Gloucester.

Hard cheeses
These include Cheddar, Cheshire, Edam and Double Gloucester. These are pressed well to remove most of the whey. Less well pressed hard cheeses are softer and crumblier in texture, e.g. Caerphilly, Lancashire and Wensleydale.

Some cheeses have *Penicillium* moulds introduced into them to make them blue-veined, e.g. Blue Stilton, Danish Blue. Moulds can be used on the outside of some cheeses, e.g. Brie and Camembert. These moulds are harmless and enhance the flavour of the cheese.

Edam, Gouda, Brie and Camembert all have lower fat contents than other hard cheeses.

Cottage cheese
This is made from skimmed milk. A starter is added to separate the curds from the whey. It has a lower fat content than hard cheese and often contains added ingredients, e.g. pineapple, chives or prawns.

Curd cheese

This is a soft creamy cheese with an acid flavour. It has a higher fat content than cottage cheese but lower than cream cheese. Curd cheese can be successfully used as a substitute for cream cheese. Pineapple, chopped spring onions or chives can be added to curd cheese.

Cream cheese

This is made from cream and has a very high fat content. The protein content is low and so it should not be used as a substitute for other cheeses.

EGGS

Eggs are very versatile and can be used in a number of ways in food preparation. Eggs hold air when whisked and can be used to make whisked sponge cakes and meringues. They enable mixtures to be set, e.g. in egg custards or savoury flans. They can also be eaten in their own right in a variety of ways, e.g. boiled, poached, scrambled. Eggs can also be used to coat, bind and glaze food.

Storing eggs

Eggs should be stored in a cool place, not necessarily in the refrigerator. If eggs are stored in the refrigerator they should be kept in the special compartments in the door, not in the body of the refrigerator. Warm eggs to room temperature prior to use, especially before baking as they mix more easily. Eggs should always be stored with the pointed end downwards.

Eggs will keep for 2–3 weeks in a cool place. Eggs can be tested for freshness by putting them in a bowl of water. An egg that sinks is fresh; if an egg floats on the surface it is stale as this indicates that a lot of the moisture has evaporated through the shell making the air space bigger and the egg lighter. A fresh egg that is cracked on to a plate will have a jelly-like white and a firm prominent yolk in the centre. A stale egg will look watery and flat with the yolk not centrally placed.

Welsh rarebit

200 g (8 oz) Cheddar cheese, grated

25 g (1 oz) margarine

1 level teaspoon dry mustard

salt and pepper

4 tablespoons milk

slices of wholemeal toast

METHOD:
1. Place all the ingredients (except the toast) in a pan and heat very gently until a creamy mixture is obtained.
2. Pour over the toast and place under a hot grill until golden brown. The toast could be cut into shapes for children.

Cheese soufflé (serves 3)

3 eggs   125 ml (6 oz) milk
25 g (1 oz) margarine   75 g (3 oz) cheese, grated
25 g (1 oz) flour   salt and pepper

FIG. 11.10

METHOD:
1. Oil a 15 cm (6 in.) soufflé dish. Separate the eggs.
2. Melt the margarine in a pan, add the flour, cook for 2 minutes, stirring constantly with a wooden spoon. Gradually add the milk, a little at a time.
3. Cool the sauce slightly, add the cheese. Add the egg yolks one at a time, beating well.
4. Whisk the egg whites until stiff, gently fold into the mixture.
5. Bake at 180 °C/Gas Mark 4 for 30 minutes, until golden brown in colour (see Fig. 11.10).

Cheese sauce

500 ml (1 pt) milk   75 g (3 oz) Cheddar cheese,
25 g (1 oz) flour   grated
25 g (1 oz) margarine   1 level teaspoon dry mustard
                          salt and pepper

METHOD:
1. Melt the margarine in a pan, add the flour, mixing well.
2. Gradually add the milk, adding a little at a time. Cook for 2 minutes.
3. Stir in the grated cheese, when melted add the mustard and season to taste.

This can be used to pour over fish and vegetables.

For a coating cheese sauce: use 50 g (2 oz) margarine and 50 g (2 oz) flour.

Cauliflower cheese
1 cauliflower
1 pt coating cheese sauce
25 g (1 oz) cheese, finely grated

METHOD:
1. Boil the cauliflower in salted water for 15 minutes.
2. Drain and place in an ovenproof dish. Pour the sauce over the cauliflower, sprinkle with the grated cheese.
3. Place under a hot grill until the cheese melts and browns.

Cheese straws
100 g (4 oz) wholemeal flour
100 g (4 oz) soft margarine
100 g (4 oz) cheese, finely grated

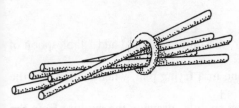

FIG. 11.11

METHOD:
1. Rub the margarine into the flour, add the cheese and knead to form a soft dough.
2. If the dough is very soft, chill in the refrigerator for 15 minutes.
3. Roll the dough out on a floured board. Cut into long strips or cut out into various shapes for children.
4. Place on a lightly oiled baking sheet and bake at 190 °C/Gas Mark 5 for about 10–15 minutes. Cool on a wire rack (see Fig. 11.11).

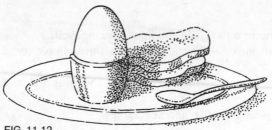

FIG. 11.12

Boiled eggs

METHOD:

1. Place eggs in boiling water with a spoon, lower the heat and cook for 3 minutes.
2. Hard-boiled eggs should boil for 10 minutes. Place under cold running water for a few minutes as soon as they are ready. This prevents a black discolouring rim from forming around the outside of the yolk. Remove the shell when cool (see Fig. 11.12).

Scrambled eggs

METHOD:

1. Melt a knob of margarine in a saucepan. Whisk two eggs with 2 tablespoons of milk, season to taste.
2. Add the eggs to the margarine and heat gently, stirring all the time until the mixture thickens.
3. Serve on wholemeal toast.

Plain omelette (serves 1)

METHOD:

1. Whisk two eggs together, season to taste and add 1 tablespoon of water.
2. Heat a knob of margarine in a frying pan, when melted add the eggs.
3. Stir gently with a wooden spatula, drawing the mixture from the sides to centre as it sets. Let the liquid egg from the centre run to the sides. When the egg has set, continue cooking until it is golden brown underneath.
4. Using a spatula fold the omelette in three, turn on to a plate with the folded side underneath. Serve immediately.

Variations:

• Add 1 teaspoon of mixed herbs to the eggs before cooking.
• Add 40 g (1½ oz) grated cheese to the eggs before cooking.
• Add 50 g (2 oz) cooked mushrooms in the centre of the omelette before folding.

- Add 50 g (2 oz) diced ham in the centre of the omelette before folding.

Egg custard (serves 3)

2 eggs	2 level tablespoons castor sugar
375 ml (¾ pt) milk	nutmeg

METHOD:
1. Beat the eggs and sugar together.
2. Gently warm the milk, pour it on to the eggs and beat well.
3. Strain the mixture in to a lightly greased pie dish (500 ml/1 pt).
4. Place the dish in a roasting tin, add warm water to come half-way up the tin.
5. Sprinkle grated nutmeg on to the custard, bake for about 50 minutes at 160 °C/Gas Mark 3.

Cheese and egg recipes in other sections include: macaroni cheese (p. 130), savoury flans (p. 151), cheese scones (p. 142) and pizza (p. 155).

RICE AND PASTA

Rice and pasta are becoming more popular in the UK as an alternative to bread and potatoes as the 'filler' in a meal. Rice is the staple food of many people in the East, especially southern India and China. Pasta is produced and eaten in Italy.

RICE

Rice is available as polished or brown rice. Brown rice is the whole rice grain which contains the bran layers and germ. These are good sources of B vitamins and minerals. Polished rice, which is more widely available, has all the bran layers and germ removed. This leaves a 'polished' or white rice which is almost entirely starch. Brown rice is increasing in popularity as it not only contains more vitamins and minerals but it is also a valuable source of dietary fibre.

Size of grain

Short grain or pudding rice
This type of rice becomes sticky and soft when cooked and is best suited for rice puddings.

Long grain rice

For example patna or Basmati rice, these are 4–5 times longer than they are broad. This rice stays fluffy and separates when cooked. It is used for savoury dishes. Basmati rice is grown in India. It has a good flavour and is the best type of rice to serve with curry.

COOKING LONG GRAIN RICE:

Allow 50 g (2 oz) per person. For two people place 100 g rice in a thick-based pan with 250 ml (½ pt) salted water, bring to the boil and cover with a tight-fitting lid. Reduce the heat and simmer for 15 minutes, without disturbing. Remove from the heat and fluff the grains with a fork. All the liquid should be absorbed. For brown rice, cook for 40–45 minutes.

PASTA

Pasta is made from durum wheat which is ground into flour and mixed with water. It is made into different shapes and dried. Some of the more popular shapes are: macaroni, spaghetti, noodles, lasagne, ravioli, cannelloni and various fancy shapes including bows, shells and twists (see Fig. 11.13).

Pasta can be made from white or wholemeal flour. The latter contains more dietary fibre. Sometimes egg can be added to the dough or spinach to make green pasta, e.g. lasagne verdi.

TO COOK PASTA:

Allow 50–75 g (2–3 oz) per person. Cook the pasta in plenty of boiling salted water. Boil vigorously without covering. This prevents the pasta from sticking. Oil (1 tablespoon) is also added to large pieces of pasta to prevent them from sticking. Cooking time depends on the size of the pasta. For long spaghetti, hold the strands in the pan and as the ends soften, coil them around the edge of the pan (Fig. 11.14).

It is preferable to use brown rice and wholemeal pasta in the following recipes.

Chicken curry (serves 4)

400 g (1 lb) cooked chicken, diced
100 g (4 oz) onion
2 cloves garlic, crushed
2 tablespoons oil

1 dessertspoon curry powder
1 tablespoon tomato purée
250 ml (½ pt) chicken stock
200 g (8 oz) long grain rice

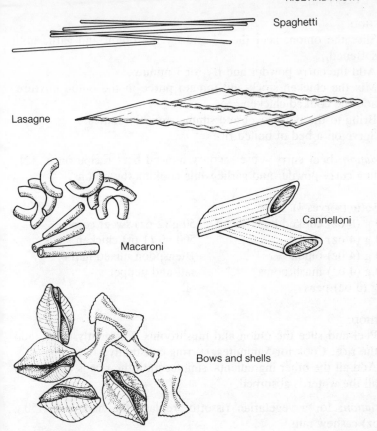

Spaghetti

Lasagne

Macaroni

Cannelloni

Bows and shells

FIG. 11.13 Types of pasta

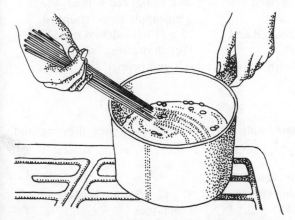

FIG. 11.14 Coiling the spaghetti around the edge of a pan

METHOD:
1. Slice the onion, heat the oil and fry the onion and garlic until softened.
2. Add the curry powder and fry for 1 minute.
3. Mix the chicken stock and tomato purée in the onion mixture, add the cooked chicken.
4. Bring to the boil, cover and simmer for 20 minutes.
5. Serve on a bed of boiled rice.

Variation: beef curry – use savoury minced beef recipe on p. 121, adding curry powder and garlic while cooking the onions.

Rissotto (serves 4)

200 g (8 oz) cooked ham, diced	50 g (2 oz) sweet corn
100 g (4 oz) rice	500 ml (1 pt) chicken stock
100 g (4 oz) onion	1 teaspoon mixed herbs
100 g (4 oz) mushrooms	salt and pepper
75 g (3 oz) peas	oil

METHOD:
1. Peel and slice the onion and mushrooms. Fry gently in oil, add the rice. Cook for 5 minutes, stirring constantly.
2. Add all the other ingredients, simmer until the rice is tender and all the water is absorbed.

Variation: for a vegetarian rissotto, replace the ham with 150 g (6 oz) cashew nuts.

Rice salad (serves 4)

100 g (4 oz) rice, cooked and cooled	50 g (2 oz) red pepper, diced
50 g (2 oz) peas, cooked and cooled	2 pineapple rings, chopped
50 g (2 oz) sweet corn, cooked and cooled	25 g (1 oz) sultanas or raisins
	French dressing (see p. 137)
	salt and pepper

METHOD:
1. Mix all the ingredients together, toss in French dressing and season to taste.

Macaroni cheese (serves 4)

500 ml (1 pt) coating cheese sauce (see p. 124)	50 g (2 oz) grated cheese
200 g (8 oz) macaroni	2 tomatoes

METHOD:
1. Cook the macaroni in salted water until tender. Drain well.
2. Mix the macaroni with the cheese sauce. Pour into an ovenproof dish. Sprinkle with grated cheese and garnish with tomato slices.
3. Bake at 180 °C/Gas Mark 4 until the cheese is golden brown.

Spaghetti bolognese (serves 4)

1 quantity savoury minced beef (see p. 121)
1 large tin of tomatoes, drained
½ teaspoon garlic powder

1 teaspoon mixed herbs
200 g (8 oz) spaghetti
parmesan cheese

FIG. 11.15

METHOD:
1. Add the drained tomatoes, garlic and herbs to the savoury mince, cook for 5 minutes further.
2. Boil the spaghetti, drain well.
3. Serve the spaghetti on individual plates in a circle with the bolognese sauce in the middle. Sprinkle with parmesan cheese if desired (see Fig. 11.15).

Lasagne (serves 4)

1 quantity bolognese sauce (above)
1 quantity cheese sauce (see p. 124) plus 50 g (2 oz) grated cheese

150 g (6 oz) lasagne
1 tablespoon of oil

METHOD:
1. Cook the lasagne in boiling salted water, with the oil to keep the leaves separate. Drain well.
2. Place a layer of the bolognese sauce in the bottom of an ovenproof dish, then a layer of cheese sauce, then lasagne. Continue building layers, ending with lasagne and cheese sauce on the top. Cover with grated cheese.
3. Bake at 180 °C/Gas Mark 4 for 40 minutes until golden brown.

Spaghetti carbonara (serves 2)

200 g (8 oz) spaghetti
    (other types of pasta,
    e.g. tagliatelle or shapes
    are also suitable)

100 g (4 oz) bacon
2 eggs
75 g (3 oz) onion, sliced
50 g (2 oz) grated cheese
pepper

METHOD:

1. Cook the spaghetti in boiling salted water, drain well.
2. Chop the bacon and fry in a frying pan. When almost cooked add the onion, continue cooking until the onion is soft.
3. Beat the eggs well, add the cheese and pepper.
4. Return the pasta to the saucepan, and on a gentle heat mix in the bacon and onion and the egg mixture. Continue stirring until the eggs set. Serve on individual plates.

Rice and pasta recipes included in other sections: lentil lasagne (p. 134).

PULSES

The term 'pulses' is the collective name for the many varieties of peas, beans and lentils. Pulses are a good and economical source of protein (low biological value), carbohydrate, B vitamins and iron. They are also low in fat and high in fibre and so are a useful addition to a healthy diet. They can be used as a protein source in their own right or to extend animal protein.

The most popular type of pulse vegetable eaten are baked beans (haricot beans) but other types of pulses are becoming more popular.

TYPES OF PULSES

Beans

Adzuki beans: small red beans with a nutty flavour.
Black-eyed beans: small cream-coloured beans with a black spot.
Butter beans: large flat cream-coloured beans.
Haricot beans: mainly seen as canned baked beans.
Mung beans: tiny round green beans which when germinated grow into beansprouts.
Red kidney beans: bright red beans in a kidney shape. Often eaten in chilli con carne.
Soya beans: small round pale beans.

Peas
Chick peas: small and pale gold in colour. In the Middle East they are puréed and made into dips.
Split peas: halved dried peas which can be green or yellow in colour.

Lentils
Split lentils: halved lentils which are bright orange in colour. Used for soups and stews.
Whole lentils: either brown or green. They retain their shape on cooking.
There are many more less popular varieties of pulses available (see Fig. 11.16).

FIG. 11.16 Types of pulses

PREPARATION AND COOKING

Pulses are usually dried and so should be soaked before cooking. This can either be overnight in cold water or boiled for 5 minutes and left for 1 hour. Drain the water and rinse the pulses. Cook in fresh water, without the addition of salt as this makes the pulses tough. All pulses but especially red kidney beans should be boiled for 10 minutes before simmering to destroy certain toxins which may be present and which can cause food poisoning.

Lentils and split peas do not need to be soaked before cooking.

Cooking times

These may vary considerably.

Adzuki beans, mung beans and split lentils	30 minutes
Black-eyed beans, split peas	45 minutes
Butter beans, whole lentils, red kidney beans	1 hour
Chick peas and haricot beans	1½ hours
Soya beans	3–4 hours

Pressure cooking (at H/15 lb) reduces the cooking times to one-third of the stated times.

Lentil lasagne (serves 4)

150 g (6 oz) whole lentils
100 g (4 oz) onion, peeled and
  chopped
2 cloves garlic, crushed
2 tablespoons oil
250 ml (½ pt) water
salt, pepper, mixed herbs

1 large tin of tomatoes, drained
200 g (8 oz) lasagne
500 ml (1 pt) coating cheese
  sauce (see p. 124)
50 g (2 oz) grated cheese

METHOD:

1. Wash the lentils. Fry the onion and garlic in oil in a saucepan for 10 minutes, add the lentils.
2. Pour the water in the pan and continue cooking for 45 minutes or until the lentils are cooked. (Do not let the mixture dry out.)
3. Season with salt, pepper and mixed herbs. Add the tinned tomatoes.
4. Cook the lasagne in boiling salted water, with a little oil added.
5. Place alternate layers of lentil mixture, cheese sauce and lasagne in an ovenproof dish. End with a layer of lasagne and cheese sauce. Sprinkle the grated cheese on top of the cheese sauce.
6. Bake at 200 °C/Gas Mark 6 for 40 minutes.

Chilli con carne (serves 4)

½ quantity savoury minced meat
1 large tin of tomatoes, drained
½ teaspoon garlic powder

½–1 teaspoon of chilli powder
  or chilli seasoning
1 green pepper, sliced
200 g (8 oz) red kidney beans or
  1 large tin

METHOD:

1. Soak the beans overnight or by the quick method (see p. 133). Boil for 10 minutes then reduce the heat and cook until soft (but not until they disintegrate).

2. Add the tomatoes, garlic, chilli powder, pepper and beans to the savoury minced beef, adding a little water if necessary. Simmer for 15 minutes.
3. Serve with boiled rice and a green salad.

Haricot bean casserole (serves 4)

200 g (8 oz) haricot beans	50 g (2 oz) mushrooms
100 g (4 oz) onion	1 large green pepper
1 large can of tomatoes	1 clove of garlic, crushed
100 g (4 oz) carrot	salt, pepper, mixed herbs
3 sticks of celery	250 ml (½ pt) water
oil	

METHOD:
1. Soak the beans overnight or soak by the quick method (see p. 133). Rinse and simmer gently in water for about 1½ hours until tender.
2. Meanwhile, chop the onion, celery, slice the carrots, mushrooms and green pepper.
3. Fry the onion and garlic in oil, add the other vegetables, tomatoes, cooked beans, seasoning and water.
4. Transfer to a casserole dish, bake at 180 °C/Gas Mark 4 for 30 minutes, or until the vegetables are soft.
5. Serve with baked potatoes and a green salad.

Meatless shepherds pie (serves 4)

100 g (4 oz) whole lentils	1 large tin tomatoes
100 g (4 oz) split peas	salt, pepper, mixed herbs
100 g (4 oz) onion, chopped	500 g (1 lb) cooked potatoes
50 g (2 oz) mushrooms, sliced	75 g (3 oz) cheese, grated
3 sticks of celery, diced	oil
1 clove of garlic, crushed	

METHOD:
1. Wash the peas and lentils, simmer gently in water for about 1 hour until soft, and the water has been absorbed.
2. Meanwhile, fry the onion and garlic until soft, add the celery and mushrooms. Cook for 5 minutes.
3. Add the tomatoes, cooked peas and lentils, season to taste. Cook for 5 minutes, gently.

4. Add 50 g (2 oz) cheese to the mashed potatoes. Transfer the lentil mixture to an ovenproof dish, top with the potatoes, sprinkle with the remaining cheese. Bake for 25 minutes at 180 °C/Gas Mark 4.

Pulse vegetable recipes included in other sections: lentil soup (p. 110), three-bean salad (p. 139).

VEGETABLES

Vegetables are important in the diet as they provide vitamins, minerals and dietary fibre. Generally they have a low energy value; this is increased when fat is added, as in chips and roast potatoes. If these are eaten it is healthier to cook them in vegetable oil rather than animal fat.

Vegetables can be eaten raw or cooked; raw vegetables, e.g. carrots and celery, can be given to children in between meals instead of sugary and fatty snacks. They can also be used to make a variety of interesting salads.

STORING AND COOKING VEGETABLES

- Avoid buying damaged, wilted and bruised vegetables.
- Keep vegetables in a cool airy place. Salad vegetables should be stored in the cool box in the refrigerator.
- Peel all vegetables thinly as there are more vitamins and minerals under the skin; do not peel until just before required. New potatoes and young vegetables can be eaten with their skins on.
- Do not soak vegetables before cooking, as water-soluble vitamins and minerals are lost.
- Cook vegetables quickly in a minimum quantity of *boiling* water to retain the vitamin C and folic acid (see Ch. 4).
- Cook vegetables until they are just tender, serve immediately. Vitamins are lost if vegetables are kept hot for long periods.
- Use the cooking liquid to make sauces and gravies.

Most vegetables are available throughout the year in the frozen, tinned and dried state. Most fresh vegetables are available throughout the year but at certain times they are 'in season' when they are at their best and cheapest.

Table 11.1 shows the cooking time for popular vegetables.

TABLE 11.1 Cooking times for vegetables

Vegetable	Approximate boiling time (in lightly salted boiling water)
Beans: broad	15–20 minutes
French	8 minutes
Broccoli	10 minutes
Brussels sprouts	10–15 minutes
Cabbage	8 minutes
Carrots	10 minutes
Cauliflower (whole)	15 minutes
Celery	10 minutes
Corn on the cob	10 minutes
Courgettes	10 minutes
Garden peas	10 minutes
Parsnips	20 minutes
Spinach	10 minutes
Swede	20 minutes
Turnip	15 minutes
Potatoes: boiled	20 minutes
jacket (large)	1 hour @ 200 °C/Gas Mark 6
roast	1–1½ hours @ 200 °C/Gas Mark 6

Note: Follow the manufacturer's instructions for frozen, tinned and dried vegetables.

SALADS

Salads are made from raw or cooked vegetables and fruit. They add colour, texture and flavour to a meal. They are a source of dietary fibre, vitamins and minerals.

Today there are a wide variety of salads to enjoy – they are far more interesting than just limp lettuce and slices of tomato. As well as being side dishes, salad ingredients can include protein foods such as beans, cheese, meat and fish to make them suitable for main courses.

Fresh ingredients should be used in a salad, and all vegetables should be washed and dried carefully. Salad dressings can be added, but remember if a lot of oil is used the energy value of the salad will increase dramatically.

SALAD DRESSINGS

Oil and vinegar (French dressing): put the following ingredients in a screw-top jar and shake it well:

1 tablespoon vinegar	pinch of dry mustard
2 tablespoons oil	pinch of sugar
pinch salt	pepper

Lemon juice: this can be added to salad vegetables to give a tangy flavour.

Yoghurt: this can be used on its own as a dressing or mixed with salad cream. Yoghurt mixed with chopped cucumber or onion makes a refreshing salad and accompaniment to curries.

Salad cream: this can be made more interesting by the addition of vinegar and mixed herbs, to use in potato salads, coleslaws, etc.

Green salad (serves 4)

½ lettuce
¼ cucumber, cubed
4 sticks of celery, diced

4 spring onions, finely chopped
1 green pepper, finely sliced
oil and vinegar dressing (see recipe)

METHOD:
1. Wash the lettuce and shake it dry. Tear into small piece (using the fingers as cutting lettuce makes it limp).
2. Mix all the vegetables together in a wooden salad bowl.
3. Just before serving toss in the oil and vinegar dressing.

Tomato and onion salad (serves 4)

4 tomatoes
2 spring onions
oil and vinegar dressing

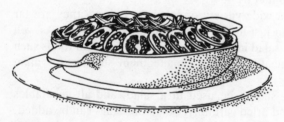

FIG. 11.17

METHOD:
1. Slice the tomatoes finely using a sharp knife.
2. Chop the spring onions finely.
3. Arrange the tomatoes on a flat dish, sprinkle the onions over the top and carefully pour over the oil and vinegar dressing (see Fig. 11.17).

Potato salad (serves 2–3)

200 g (8 oz) cooked potatoes
50 g (2 oz) onion, finely sliced
salad cream

pinch of mixed herbs
chopped chives

METHOD:
1. Carefully cut the potatoes into 1 cm (½ in.) dice. Mix with the onions.
2. Add a pinch of mixed herbs to sufficient salad cream to coat the potatoes. Carefully coat the potatoes with this dressing.
3. Serve in a small bowl, garnished with chopped chives.

Three-bean salad (serves 4)

100 g (4 oz) red kidney beans
100 g (4 oz) haricot beans
100 g (4 oz) French beans

50 g (2 oz) onion, finely
   chopped
oil and vinegar dressing
pinch of garlic powder

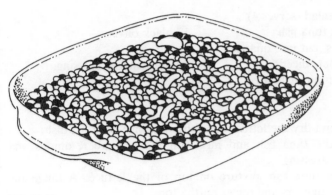

FIG. 11.18

METHOD:
1. Soak the kidney beans and haricot beans (separately) overnight or by the quick method (see p. 133). Rinse and cook separately for 1–1½ hours until tender. Remember to boil the red kidney beans for 10 minutes before simmering. Drain and allow to cool.
2. Cook the French beans, drain and cool.
3. Mix the three beans together, add the garlic powder to the oil and vinegar dressing, mix with the beans and chopped onion. Serve in a salad bowl (see Fig. 11.18).

Coleslaw (serves 4)

¼ white cabbage, finely shredded
4 carrots, grated
4 sticks of celery, finely sliced
50 g (2 oz) onion, grated
salt and pepper

2 red apples, finely chopped (leave the skins on)
25 g (1 oz) walnuts, chopped
salad cream and vinegar in equal quantities

METHOD:
1. Mix all the ingredients together in a bowl.
2. Mix the salad cream and vinegar together, season to taste.
3. Add the dressing to the coleslaw, mixing well. Serve in a salad bowl.

Variations: add different types of fruit, e.g. pineapple, tangerine segments, sultanas and chopped dates to the coleslaw. Vegetables such as green and red pepper, peas and sweet corn can be added. Use a yoghurt or oil and vinegar dressing in place of the dressing used in the recipe. The variations are endless!

Tuna fish salad (serves 4)

1 large tin tuna fish
4 tomatoes, cut into quarters
¼ cucumber, diced
4 spring onions, chopped

12 black olives
¼ lettuce
oil and vinegar dressing

METHOD:
1. Wash and dry the lettuce carefully. Arrange on a flat dish.
2. Flake the tuna fish and mix with the cucumber, onions and French dressing.
3. Pile the tuna fish mixture on top of the lettuce. Arrange the tomato quarters and olives on the top.

QUESTIONS

1. List the nutrients found in white and oily fish.
2. Which cookery methods would you choose to cook the following: fillet of cod, rump steak, pork chops, chicken breasts. Give reasons for your choice.
3. What are the differences between Double Gloucester and cottage cheeses?
4. How should eggs be stored? How do you know if an egg is fresh?

5. Why are brown rice and wholemeal pasta healthier?
6. Why do most pulses have to be soaked prior to cooking?
7. List the special points to remember when cooking vegetables.

BAKING

SCONES AND BISCUITS

Scones and biscuits are easy to make. They are cheaper and have a better flavour than their bought counterparts.

Points to remember
For scones:
- Make sure that the dough is rolled out to at least 2 cm (¾ in.) thickness so that they rise sufficiently.
- Place on the top shelf of a large oven.

For biscuits:
- Do not use a baking tray with high sides as this will result in uneven cooking.
- Oil the tray well and leave enough space in between the biscuits as they usually spread.
- After cooking leave the biscuits on the tray for only a few minutes to prevent them from sticking. The biscuits should be soft; they will become crisp when cooled.

Plain scones (makes 8–10)

200 g (8 oz) self-raising flour or wholemeal flour + 2 teaspoons baking powder	150 ml (¼ pt) milk pinch of salt
50 g (2 oz) margarine	25 g (1 oz) caster sugar

FIG. 11.19

METHOD:
1. Sift the flour in a bowl or mix the baking powder into the wholemeal flour.
2. Rub in the margarine, using the fingertips.
3. Add the sugar and salt.

4. Using a metal spoon, gradually mix in the milk to form a soft dough.
5. Turn the dough on to a floured surface and roll out to 2 cm (¾ in.) thickness. Cut into rounds using a pastry cutter, or use animal or other shapes for children.
6. Place on an oiled baking sheet and bake at 220 °C/Gas Mark 7 for 12–15 minutes (see Fig. 11.19).

Variations:

Fruit scones: add 40 g (1½ oz) dried fruit with the sugar and salt. Use a beaten egg plus milk to 150 ml (¼ pt) instead of all milk for richer scones.

Cheese scones: add 75 g (3 oz) finely grated cheese in place of the sugar, at stage 3.

Shortbread

150 g (6 oz) plain flour (or ½ plain and ½ wholemeal)
100 g (4 oz) margarine
50 g (2 oz) castor sugar

FIG. 11.20

METHOD:

1. Put the flour in a bowl, rub in the margarine, stir in the sugar.
2. Knead the dough together.
3. Roll out to 1 cm (just under ½ in.) thick, cut into rounds with a cutter, fingers or fancy-shaped cutters for children.
4. Place on an oiled baking sheet, bake at 170 °C/Gas Mark 3 for 15–20 minutes.
5. Place on a wire tray, when cooled sprinkle with extra sugar, if desired (see Fig. 11.20).

Plain biscuits (makes about 35)

200 g self-raising flour
  or 100 g (4 oz) self-raising
  flour + 100 g (4 oz)
  wholemeal flour + 1 teaspoon
  baking powder

100 g (4 oz) castor sugar
100 g (4 oz) margarine
1 egg, beaten

METHOD:

1. Mix the flour or flours and baking powder in a bowl with the sugar.

2. Rub in the margarine until the mixture resembles breadcrumbs.
3. Add the beaten egg. If the mixture is a little dry, add a few drops of milk.
4. Roll out thinly and cut into rounds with a pastry cutter or into fancy shapes for children.
5. Place on an oiled baking sheet and bake at 170 °C/Gas Mark 3 for 15 minutes.

Variations:
• Coat the biscuits with melted chocolate.
• Pipe on children's names or initials on to round biscuits using glacé icing.
• Pipe around the edges of animal biscuits, pipe on eyes, etc.
• For currant biscuits: add 2 tablespoons of currants before adding the egg.

CAKES

There are four main methods which can be used when making cakes. These are: (1) rubbing-in; (2) creaming; (3) whisking; and (4) melting.

POINTS TO REMEMBER

• Weigh the ingredients carefully, do not try to alter any of the proportions in the recipe.
• Always use self-raising flour or plain flour with added baking powder. Cakes made from wholemeal flour will need extra baking powder. Strong flours are not intended for cake-making.
• Use the correct tin size (stated in the recipe), otherwise the size of the finished cake and the cooking time will alter.
• Always line cake tins with greaseproof paper and oil so that the cakes can be removed without breaking. Non-stick cake tins should be lightly oiled and dusted with flour.
• Leave the cakes in their tins for 5–10 minutes to set, turn out on a wire tray and leave to cool.
• Properly baked cakes should shrink slightly away from the sides of the tin, be firm to the touch and evenly browned. A skewer inserted into the centre should come out clean.
• Always make sure that the cake is cold before decorating or storing.

RUBBING-IN METHOD

This is a very easy method which can be used for plain cakes, especially those containing dried fruit.

There is usually half the quantity of fat to flour in this method. The fat is rubbed into the flour with the fingertips until it resembles breadcrumbs. The other ingredients are then added. This method is also used for shortcrust pastry, scones, biscuits and crumble mixtures.

Rock buns (make 8–10)

200 g (8 oz) self-raising flour or 200 g (8 oz) wholemeal flour + 2½ teaspoons baking powder
100 g (4 oz) castor sugar

100 g (4 oz) margarine
75 g (3 oz) currants
1 egg, milk to mix

FIG. 11.21

METHOD:
1. Mix the flour or flour and baking powder in a bowl, add the sugar.
2. Rub in the margarine until the mixture resembles breadcrumbs.
3. Add the currants, mix to a stiff dough with beaten egg and about 1 tablespoon of milk.
4. Place on an oiled baking sheet in rough heaps.
5. Bake at 200 °C/Gas Mark 6 for 20 minutes (see Fig. 11.21).

Fruit loaf

150 g (6 oz) self-raising flour or wholemeal flour + 3 teaspoons baking powder
2 teaspoons mixed spice
75 g (3 oz) margarine

75 g (3 oz) castor sugar
100 g (4 oz) mixed dried fruit
1 egg
75 ml (3 oz) milk

METHOD:
1. Put the flour or flour and baking powder plus the mixed spice into a bowl. Rub in the margarine.
2. Stir in the sugar and dried fruit.
3. Beat the egg and add to the mixture with the milk.
4. Place in a small oiled and lined loaf tin, bake at 180 °C/Gas Mark 4 for 1¼ hours or until a skewer comes out clean.

Date and walnut loaf

100 g (4 oz) stoned dates
40 g (1½ oz) walnuts
300 g (¾ lb) self-raising flour
  or wholemeal flour + 3
  teaspoons baking powder

100 g (4 oz) margarine
100 g (4 oz) castor sugar
2 eggs
50 ml (2 oz) milk

METHOD:
1. Chop the dates and walnuts.
2. In a bowl, rub the margarine into the flour or flour and baking powder. Add the sugar, dates and walnuts.
3. Beat the egg, add to the mixture with the milk, adding more milk if the mixture is too dry. Pour into a large oiled and lined loaf tin.
4. Bake at 180 °C/Gas Mark 4 for 1 hour.

CREAMING METHOD (ALL-IN-ONE)

In this method equal quantities of fat, sugar and flour are used. Traditionally the fat and sugar are beaten or 'creamed' together until pale, eggs are gradually beaten into the mixture and the flour is folded in. A quicker method is the 'all-in-one' method, when all the ingredients are mixed together at once. Soft margarine is more successful than block margarine for this method. With an electric mixer an all-in-one cake can be made in minutes.

Wholemeal flour with baking powder can be used although a 50 per cent mixture of self-raising and wholemeal flours will give better results.

All-in-one cake

100 g (4 oz) self-raising flour
  or 50 g (2 oz) self-raising
  flour, 50 g (2 oz) wholemeal
  flour + 1 teaspoon baking
  powder

100 g (4 oz) soft margarine
100 g (4 oz) castor sugar
2 eggs

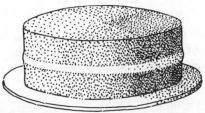

FIG. 11.22

METHOD:

1. Add all the ingredients in a bowl and mix together with an electric mixer.
2. If the mixture does not drop off a spoon easily, add a few drops of milk.
3. Pour into an oiled and lined 18 cm (7 in.) cake tin, making sure the mixture is level. (Or use two 18 cm (7 in.) sandwich tins.)
4. Bake at 180 °C/Gas Mark 4 for 25 minutes. Cool slightly, turn out on to a wire tray (see Fig. 11.22).

Variations:

Chocolate cake: add 2 tablespoons cocoa powder to the ingredients. Extra milk will be needed.

Orange cake: add the grated rind of one orange plus the juice.

Coffee and walnut cake: add 50 g (2 oz) chopped walnuts plus 1 tablespoon of instant coffee dissolved in a little hot water.

Fairy cakes: spoon the mixture into paper cases (about 12). For a less rich mixture use 150 g (6 oz) flour, this will make about 18. Fairy cakes take about 15 minutes to cook (see Fig. 11.23).

FIG. 11.23

Icing

Glacé icing: this is sieved icing sugar with water added to form a stiff paste. Food colourings, instant coffee melted in hot water, and food flavourings can be added. Use it to decorate the top of large and small cakes.

Butter icing: add double the quantity of sieved icing sugar to soft margarine. Beat well. Flavours and colours can be used as for glacé icing. It can be used to sandwich cakes together and to pipe decorations.

Fondant icing: this can be used to cover cakes, especially novelty cakes for children's parties. It can be bought ready made.

WHISKING METHOD

In this method eggs and sugar are whisked until they have at least doubled in volume and are pale in colour. The mixture should be thick enough to leave a trail that remains for 10 seconds when the whisk is removed. An electric mixer is almost essential for this method. Use eggs at room temperature; eggs straight from the refrigerator take longer to whisk. The flour, which should always be well sieved, is then gently folded into the mixture, using a metal spoon. This will maintain the volume of the mixture.

As whisked sponges do not contain fat they soon become stale and should be eaten within 2 days of baking or should be frozen.

Wholemeal flour can partially replace the plain flour in this method. Total replacement will result in a heavy rubber sponge. As they do not contain fat, whisked sponges have lower energy values than other cakes.

Whisked sponge – basic recipe
2 eggs
50 g (2 oz) castor sugar
50 g (2 oz) plain flour

METHOD:
1. Whisk the eggs and sugar together until thick (see above).
2. Fold in the flour using a metal spoon.

Uses:
Swiss roll: pour the mixture into a lined Swiss roll tin 18 × 30 cm (7 × 12 in.). Bake for 8–10 minutes at 200 °C/Gas Mark 6. When the Swiss roll is cooked, tip it on to greaseproof paper, lightly covered in sugar. Trim the edges, spread with melted jam and roll up, using the paper to help (see Fig. 11.24).

FIG. 11.24

Sandwich cake: use a three-egg mixture (i.e. with 75 g (3 oz) sugar and flour), pour into a 20 cm (8 in.) oiled and lined sandwich tin. Bake at 180 °C/Gas Mark 4 for 40 minutes. When cool, sandwich with jam and dust the top with icing sugar, or an icing on p. 146.

Fruit flan: use a three-egg mixture (see above) to fill a 20 cm (8 in.) flan ring. When cooled, fill with fruit tinned in fruit juice (e.g. apricots, peaches, pineapples, mandarin oranges) or fresh summer fruit such as strawberries or raspberries. Arrange the fruit neatly. Use 125 ml (¼ pt) water or fruit juice from the tin, 1 teaspoon of arrowroot + 1 teaspoon sugar to make a glaze. Heat the ingredients slowly in a pan, stirring until thick. Cool slightly before coating the fruit with the glaze. Serve with ice-cream or fresh cream for special occasions (see Fig. 11.25).

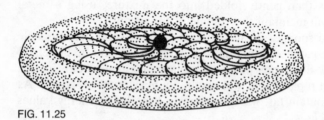

FIG. 11.25

MELTING METHOD

This is a quick, easy method of cake-making where the fat, sugar, syrup or treacle are melted together in a pan. This is added to the dry ingredients, with eggs. Plain flour and bicarbonate of soda are used. Wholemeal flour can be used totally instead of plain flour. This method is used to make gingerbread. When fresh, gingerbread often has a hard surface but if it is kept for 2 days before eating the surface softens, as well as the flavour developing.

Gingerbread

200 g (8 oz) plain flour or
  wholemeal flour
2 rounded teaspoons ground
  ginger
½ teaspoon bicarbonate of soda
100 g (4 oz) treacle

100 g (4 oz) sugar
100 g (4 oz) margarine
1 egg with enough milk to make
  up to 125 ml (¼ pt)

METHOD:
1. Melt the syrup, sugar and treacle gently over a low heat.
2. Beat the egg in the milk, sieve all the dry ingredients together.

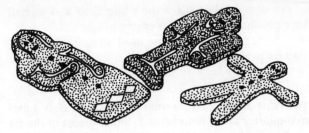

FIG. 11.26

3. Pour the treacle mixture on to the flour, mix well.
4. Add the egg and milk, a little at a time, beating well.
5. Pour into an 18 cm (7 in.) square tin which has been oiled and lined.
6. Bake at 170 °C/Gas Mark 3 for 1 hour.

Variation (gingerbread people): use the recipe above but bake in a Swiss roll tin (oiled and lined). When cool, use gingerbread men and women cutters to form the shapes. Make up some glacé icing (see p. 146) which is very stiff and pipe around the edges of the people. Fill in eyes and buttons if desired. This makes fairly soft gingerbread people as traditional recipes are often hard, especially for young children (see Fig. 11.26).

PASTRY

People often find it difficult to make good pastry. If you do not succeed initially, do not give up as practice will make perfect.

POINTS TO REMEMBER

- Handle the pastry lightly, do not over-rub the fat in the flour, over-knead or roll out too many times. If the pastry is difficult to handle or is too soft, chill it in the refrigerator for 20 minutes before rolling out.
- Do not add too much water.
- Bake in a hot oven.

TYPES OF PASTRY

Shortcrust
This is the most widely used. Half fat to flour is used; the fat is rubbed into the flour, and water is added. Plain flour is used;

wholemeal flour can completely replace the white flour and a small quantity of baking powder will make the pastry lighter.

Margarine or solid vegetable oil can be used alone or in combination, depending on personal preference.

Rough-puff pastry

This type of pastry is quite easy to make, although it is time-consuming. Three-quarter fat to flour is used. Small pieces of the fat are added to the flour without rubbing in. Water is added to form a soft dough. The pastry is rolled out on a floured surface into an oblong and folded. By continuous rolling and folding the fat is distributed into the flour. The folding creates layers which separate on cooking. Wholemeal flour can partially replace the white flour. The fat used should be block margarine and/or solid vegetable oil.

Other types of pastry are:
• Suet pastry: using shredded suet (this contains a high proportion of saturated fat).
• Choux pastry: used to make choux buns and éclairs.
• Hot water crust pastry: used for meat pies.

Fruit pie (serves 4–6)

Shortcrust pastry:
200 g (8 oz) flour
pinch of salt
100 g (4 oz) fat
water to mix

For the filling:
500 g (1 lb) fruit, e.g. cooking apples
sugar to taste

METHOD:
1. Make the pastry by rubbing in the fat into the flour and salt, until the mixture resembles breadcrumbs. Add sufficient cold water to form a soft dough. Leave to chill.
2. Prepare the fruit, e.g. for apples peel, core and slice thinly.
3. Oil an 18 cm (7 in.) pie dish. Divide the pastry in two and roll out one half. Use to line the base of the pie dish. Spread the fruit over the pastry, sprinkle with sugar. Damp the edges of the pastry.
4. Roll out the rest of the pastry, use it to cover the pie. Seal the edges. Use any trimmings to decorate the top, e.g. pastry leaves.
5. Bake at 190 °C/Gas Mark 5 for about 40 minutes.

Variations:
• Add 2 teaspoons cinnamon plus 25 g (1 oz) sultanas to the apples.
• Use other fruit, e.g. rhubarb, plums, gooseberries, blackcurrants, strawberries.

Savoury flan (serves 4–6)

Shortcrust pastry:
100 g (4 oz) flour
pinch of salt
50 g (2 oz) fat
water to mix

For the filling:
2 eggs
125 ml (¼ pt) milk
75 g (3 oz) onion
75 g (3 oz) bacon
50 g (2 oz) cheese, grated
1 tomato
salt, pepper

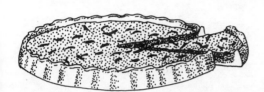

FIG. 11.27

METHOD:
1. Make the pastry as shown above. Leave to chill.
2. Meanwhile, prepare the filling. Chop the bacon into small pieces, fry in a non-stick frying pan (or use a little oil), add finely chopped onion, cook until the onion is soft. Beat the eggs, add the milk, cheese and seasoning. Add the bacon and onion to the egg mixture.
3. Use the pastry to line an 18 cm (7 in.) flan ring or flan dish. Pour the filling into the flan, garnish with sliced tomato.
4. Bake at 190 °C/Gas Mark 5 for 30–40 minutes.

Variations:
• Use extra cheese and onion to make a cheese and onion flan.
• Tuna flan – omit the cheese and bacon and add one small can of tuna fish (flaked).
Savoury flans can be made in individual bun tins or foil containers for packed meals or for children's parties (see Fig. 11.27).

Corned beef pasties

Shortcrust pastry:
200 g (8 oz) flour
100 g (4 oz) fat
pinch of salt
water to mix

For the filling:
1 small tin corned beef
150 g (6 oz) cooked and mashed
    potatoes
50 g (2 oz) onion
salt and pepper

METHOD:
1. Make the pastry as shown above.
2. Break up the corned beef with a fork, mix into the mashed potatoes. Grate the onion finely, add to the potato mixture, season to taste.
3. Roll the pastry out, cut out circles using a plate or saucer.
4. Place even amounts of filling on one half of each pasty. Dampen the edges with water, fold the pastry over and seal well.
5. Place on a baking sheet and bake at 190 °C/Gas Mark 5 for 25 minutes or until golden brown.

Sausage rolls
Rough-puff pastry:
200 g (8 oz) flour
pinch of salt
150 g (6 oz) fat
water to mix

For the filling:
400 g (1 lb) sausage meat
salt and pepper

FIG. 11.28

METHOD:
1. Cut the fat into small pieces, about 1 cm (½ in.) square. Make sure the fat is cold. Sieve the flour and salt together, stir in the fat.
2. Add sufficient cold water to form a soft dough (this pastry needs a lot more water than shortcrust). The dough will be very messy at this stage.
3. Carefully place on a floured board, roll out to a rectangle about 40 × 20 cm (16 × 8 in.). Fold the top third down to the middle third and the bottom third up to the middle third. Seal the edges, then turn the pastry a quarter turn.
4. Repeat stage 3 twice more (making three foldings altogether).
5. Leave the pastry in a refrigerator for 15 minutes.
6. Repeat the foldings another three times, leave to chill for a further 15 minutes.
7. Season the sausage meat. Roll out the pastry into a large thin square, cut into strips about 10 cm (4 in.) long.
8. Using floured hands, roll out the sausage meat to the same length as the pastry strips. Place it on to the pastry.

9. Dampen the edges of the pastry to seal them, fold the pastry over and seal well. Cut into 5 or 10 cm lengths (2 or 4 in.), mark the tops by snipping the pastry with a pair of scissors. Brush with milk.
10. Place on a baking tray and cook at 200 °C/Gas Mark 6 for 20 minutes (see Fig. 11.28).

The fruit pie and corned beef pasty recipes can also be made using rough-puff pastry.

Pastry recipes included in other sections: chicken and mushroom pie (p. 119), savoury minced beef pie (p. 121).

YEAST COOKERY

There is nothing difficult about cooking with yeast. Yeast is a living organism and requires warmth, food and moisture to grow. In cookery food is obtained from the flour, moisture from the liquid used and warmth by keeping all ingredients, especially the liquid, at blood temperature. The yeast converts starches to carbon dioxide which causes the bread to rise. Alcohol is also produced which evaporates on cooking. Different strains of yeast are used in brewing.

Yeast
Fresh yeast should be used within 4–5 days. It is stirred into the liquid with a small quantity of sugar and used directly.
Dried yeast has to be activated; the granules of dried yeast are added to the liquid and sugar and left for 15–20 minutes or until the liquid becomes frothy. Dried yeast which is added directly to the flour before adding liquid is also available.

Flour
The flour used in yeast cookery should be strong; this contains extra gluten which forms a better product. Strong wholemeal flour is available and makes a well-flavoured bread which is high in fibre.

Ascorbic acid or vitamin C tablets
These are added to the liquid when making bread. They strengthen the gluten when the dough is kneaded and proved (allowing the dough to rise). The dough only requires one proving when these tablets are added; traditionally two provings are necessary.

Liquid

The liquid used in bread-making should be at blood temperature, i.e. if you dip your finger into the liquid it should feel neither hot nor cold. If the liquid is too hot it will kill the yeast and if it is too cold the dough will rise very slowly.

The amount of liquid added depends on the type of flour and the temperature of the room. Wholemeal flour requires extra water. More liquid may be needed if you are working in a hot kitchen. Remember to ensure that any extra liquid added is also at blood temperature.

Margarine and salt

Margarine and salt are added for flavour.

Bread (for 1 large loaf or 18 rolls)

400 g (1 lb) strong white or wholemeal flour
1 level teaspoon salt
25 g (1 oz) margarine

15 g (½ oz) fresh yeast
250 ml (½ pt) water, at body temperature
1 ascorbic acid tablet (25 or 50 mg)

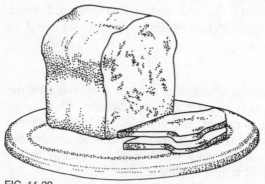

FIG. 11.29

METHOD:

1. Put the flour and salt in a bowl, rub in the margarine.
2. Mix the yeast in the warm water, add the ascorbic acid tablet, crushed.
3. Pour the yeast mixture into the flour, mix well to form a soft dough. Add more liquid if the dough is dry.
4. Turn the dough out on to a floured board, knead firmly for 10 minutes. This is done by punching, pulling and stretching the dough as vigorously as possible.

5. Shape the dough into a loaf or eighteen rolls. Place the loaf in a large oiled loaf tin or the rolls on a baking sheet.
6. Leave in a warm place to rise. The dough should double in size.
7. Bake at 230 °C/Gas Mark 8 for 40 minutes for the loaf or 15–20 minutes for the rolls (see Fig. 11.29).

Pizza

For the base:
use ½ the bread recipe
oil

For the filling:
1 large can of tomatoes, drained
1 tablespoon tomato purée .
1 teaspoon oregano
salt and pepper
100 g (4 oz) cheese
50 g (2 oz) salami
a few black olives

FIG. 11.30

METHOD:
1. Prepare dough to stage 4 above.
2. Liquidise the tomatoes, tomato purée, oregano and seasoning.
3. Roll out the dough into a large circle, brush with oil, place on baking sheet.
4. Place the tomato mixture on the dough, sprinkle the cheese over the top, arrange the salami and garnish with a few black olives.
5. Leave to prove in a warm place for 15 minutes.
6. Bake in an oven at 220 °C/Gas Mark 7 for 30 minutes, or until the base is cooked (see Fig. 11.30).

Chelsea buns (makes 8)

For the dough:
use ½ the bread recipe but
use milk instead of water

For the filling:
25 g (1 oz) margarine
75 g (3 oz) currants
25 g (1 oz) sugar

METHOD:
1. Make the dough to stage 4 of the bread recipe (p. 154).
2. Roll out into a large square, 25 × 25 cm (10 × 10 in.).

3. Warm the margarine in a small pan, brush the dough with this.
4. Sprinkle the dough with the currants and sugar. Roll the dough up like a Swiss roll. Cut into about eight slices.
5. Place in a 20 cm (8 in.) oiled cake tin. Leave to prove until they have doubled in size. (The buns should be touching.)
6. Bake at 220 °C/Gas Mark 7 for 20 minutes.
7. Warmed honey can be spread over the top of the buns while they are still hot.

HOT AND COLD PUDDINGS

There are numerous recipes for hot and cold puddings, many of which are very unhealthy! However, life would be very dull if we did not have one or two indulgences occasionally. The recipes below are intended for everyday consumption and are not overladen with sugar and cream.

Fresh fruit, cheese and biscuits, and fruit yoghurt are nutritious ways of ending a meal.

HOT PUDDINGS

Apple and blackberry crumble (serves 4)
300 g (¾ lb) cooking apples
200 g (½ lb) blackberries, fresh or frozen
50 g (2 oz) sugar

For the crumble:
100 g (4 oz) wholemeal flour
50 g (2 oz) sugar
50 g (2 oz) margarine

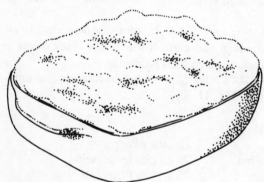

FIG. 11.31

METHOD:
1. Make the crumble by rubbing the margarine into the flour, stir in the sugar.

2. Peel and thinly slice the apples. Place the blackberries and the apples in a 1 litre (2 pt) ovenproof dish. Sprinkle with sugar.
3. Cover the fruit with the crumble mixture.
4. Bake at 190 °C/Gas Mark 5 for 35–45 minutes (see Fig. 11.31).

Variations: use different types of fruit to make a crumble, e.g. apple, apple and dried fruit, plum, rhubarb, gooseberry, frozen strawberry, apricot. Use about 500 g (1¼ lb) fruit.

Baked apple (per person)
1 large baking apple
1 dessertspoon dried fruit or dried fruit and walnuts or 2 stoned dates
1 dessertspoon brown sugar

METHOD:
1. Remove the core of each apple with a corer. Make a small slit around the centre of the apple.
2. Stand the apples in an ovenproof dish, fill the cores with dried fruit, etc. Sprinkle the sugar on the top. Add a little water in the bottom of the dish.
3. Bake at 190 °C/Gas Mark 5 for 30 minutes or until the apple is soft.

COLD PUDDINGS

Fresh fruit salad (serves 4)

1 small tin of unsweetened
   pineapple pieces
2 red apples, sliced finely
2 oranges

1 pear
1 banana
50 g (2 oz) black grapes

FIG. 11.32

METHOD:

1. Chop the apple and the pear into even-sized pieces, about the size of the pineapple. Do not peel.
2. Remove the skin and segments from the oranges (see Florida cocktail, p. 109).
3. Wash the grapes, slice in two and remove the pips.
4. Place all the fruit, except the banana, in a large glass bowl, chill. Before serving, slice the banana and add it to the salad. Serve with natural yoghurt or ice-cream (see Fig. 11.32).

Variations: any type of fresh fruit can be used, but remember to use different colours to add to the appeal of the salad. In winter stoned dates, sultanas, walnuts or almonds can be added.

Fruit fool (serves 4)
400 g (1 lb) gooseberries or rhubarb
50 g (2 oz) sugar
250 ml (½ pt) milk
1 tablespoon custard powder
1 tablespoon sugar

METHOD:

1. Gently stew the fruit with the sugar and a little water until soft. When cool, blend, removing all the gooseberry pips by sieving.
2. Heat the milk, leaving a little to blend the custard powder and sugar. Mix the milk with the custard powder and heat slowly, stirring all the time until the custard thickens.
3. Mix the fruit and custard together well, blend if necessary.
4. Pour into glass dishes, chill until ready to serve.

Variations: make half the quantity of custard and add one small pot of natural yoghurt to the custard and fruit.

Hot and cold puddings included in other sections: baked egg custard (p. 127), fruit pie (p. 150) and fruit flan (p. 148).

QUESTIONS

1. What are the rules to remember when making scones and biscuits?
2. List the different methods of making cakes. How do these differ?
3. How would you decorate fairy cakes for children? Draw some examples.

4. What are the proportions of fat and flour used in shortcrust and rough-puff pastry?
5. Why is it necessary to use warm liquid in bread-making?
6. Make a list of puddings that do not contain a lot of sugar, fat or cream.

12

COOKING FOR AND
WITH CHILDREN

Nursery nurses can be involved in cooking for children and in helping children to cook, at home or with a group in the nursery school.

The choice of food made by the nursery nurse either for the child to eat or what to cook in school can influence future food preferences. It is important that children are given healthy choices of food to eat and to prepare. There is no point in giving the children a lesson on tooth decay then making peppermint creams!

COOKING FOR CHILDREN

The basis of childhood nutrition is detailed in Chapter 6. Basic food plans for weaning babies at various stages and for toddlers are given.

When planning meals for children, e.g. the midday meal, it is a good idea to make a list each week of the foods you will give at each mealtime to ensure nutritional adequacy and to avoid repetition and monotony. Even if a child will eat fish fingers, they will soon tire of them if given everyday!

Children do not have bland palates, they will eat interesting food as long as it is not too spicy or highly flavoured with herbs. For example, a child will probably enjoy minced beef mildly spiced with curry powder, but not if it is red hot!

Ways of disguising the important foods are shown in Chapter 6.

It would be very difficult to decide not to give a child in your care sweets and chocolates, especially if their parents and relations do, but it is a good idea to restrict sweet eating to certain times of the day to reduce the acidity of the mouth to a minimum (see Ch. 2).

If a child is not eating, or for a special occasion, food can be made individually or decorated into a face, train or fort, etc. If vegetables are an integral part of the decoration it may encourage a child to eat them. Homemade fish cakes and beefburgers can be cut

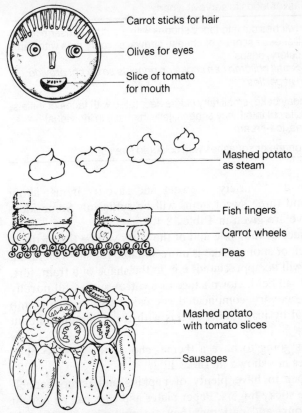

Carrot sticks for hair

Olives for eyes

Slice of tomato for mouth

Mashed potato as steam

Fish fingers

Carrot wheels

Peas

Mashed potato with tomato slices

Sausages

FIG. 12.1 Ideas for making food more attractive: (a) A face on, for example, an individual shepherds pie; (b) a fish-finger train; (c) a sausage fort

into fish or animal shapes. Figure 12.1 gives some ideas of how to decorate food.

COOKING FOR A CHILDREN'S PARTY

Parties for young children should be fun not only for the guests but also for the caterers. All the food and the table decorations should be brightly coloured. Choose food that children will be able to manage easily. Individual portions are easier to hold and look more attractive. For example, individual savoury flans are far nicer than a slice from a large flan which tends to be sloppy.

Small individual portions will also reduce waste as usually all the party guests will want to sample everything – even if it is just to take one bite and leave the rest.

TABLE 12.1:   Ideas for foods to serve at a party

Savoury	Sandwiches cut into fancy shapes with a cutter, sausage rolls, small cheese scones or cheese straws, savoury dips with carrot and celery, crisps *NB Small children can choke on peanuts so do not provide them at parties*
Sweet	Birthday cake, small fairy cakes decorated with faces or initials, biscuits cut into fancy shapes, jelly, mousse in individual dishes, ice-cream
To drink	Lemonade or squashes with coloured straws

Try and provide a variety of sweet and savoury items; about three savoury and three sweet items will be sufficient. Some ideas for foods to serve are given in Table 12.1.

The centre piece of the table and of the party will be the birthday cake. A sandwich or sponge cake is more suitable for small children. A novelty cake will be appreciated, e.g. in the shape of a train, fort, fairy castle, football field, clown's face or a cat. A successful novelty cake need not be very complicated. A cake can be made into something special by just adding sweets with the minimum amount of skill required.

If the party is going to have a theme, choose the food to fit in with it. Examples are shown in Table 12.2.

Also remember to have plenty of napkins and damp flannels available to wipe sticky fingers. Paper plates and cups can be bought in attractive colours and patterns; they are expensive but they do save having to wash up and reduce breakages to a minimum.

TABLE 12.2 Ideas for theme parties

Teddy bears' picnic Sandwiches cut into animal shapes Animal-shaped biscuits Pear mice on jelly A teddy bear cake	*Princess party* Royal sausage rolls Dainty sandwiches Crown-shaped cheese biscuits Choux pastry swans Fairy cakes with flowers A fairy tale castle cake
Ghost party Sandwiches with coloured fillings, e.g. pink curd cheese, green meat paste Cakes and biscuits with white icing Meringues in ghost shapes Ice-cream A large ghost-shaped cake	*Clown's party* Individual flans with a clown's face on each Sausage and pineapple on sticks Pinwheel sandwiches Fairy cakes Individual strawberry mousse A clown's face cake

COOKING WITH CHILDREN

Most children of nursery age and upwards enjoy cooking sessions in school, as well as at home. Not only do children gain from learning manipulative skills such as rubbing fat into flour but cooking also provides a good opportunity for the application of many other subjects taught in schools.

ORGANISATION OF COOKERY SESSIONS

Group size
Ideally the group of children chosen should be a small one, with a maximum of about six children. This will enable all the children to participate actively in the lesson. Try and do several cooking sessions so that all the children from the class have a chance at joining in.

Planning
If the children are selected in advance they can help to choose what to make and discuss the ingredients, shopping list, etc.

The choice of food to prepare depends on several factors:
- cooking facilities;
- equipment available;
- time allowed;
- interest value of the dishes.

Whatever you decide to cook, do make sure that the recipe is foolproof, does not involve any difficult skills and has been tested at home beforehand.

Cooking facilities and equipment available
First of all, check the safety regulations laid down by the local authority to make sure that these will not be infringed by the cookery session.

There should be a sink with hot and cold water available, not just a wash-hand basin. Ideally the sink should be used for cooking purposes only, if not, make sure it is thoroughly cleaned before use.

All equipment for cooking should be strong and be without sharp edges. Care should be taken with knives, any chopping or slicing involving a sharp knife should be demonstrated only, especially with young children. Blunt knives, e.g. for buttering bread, can be given to children, if carefully supervised.

The work table should either be used for cooking only or a table in everyday use should be covered with a washable plastic cover.

Even if there are no cooking facilities available it is still possible to do some 'cooking', but obviously the range is limited. With an oven available either in a small home economics unit or in the kitchen the scope for cooking is endless. However, as a precaution against accidents and to prevent fire, any recipes involving deep-fat frying or boiling sugar and water together should be avoided. Table 12.3 shows the range of dishes that can be made with different cooking facilities.

TABLE 12.3 Cooking facilities: ideas of dishes to prepare

No cooking facilities	Uncooked sweets, instant whips, milk shake, salad, sandwiches, fruit salad, icing a ready-made cake, cucumber crocodile
Electric kettle only	Jellies, hot drinks, chocolate crunchies
Hot plate only	Blancmange, hard-boiled eggs, pancakes
Full cooking facilities	Any dish which is simple and attractive

Note: Do not make sweet foods all the time!

Time allowed

The time allowed for cooking is an obvious constraint to the dishes that can be prepared. When choosing dishes, remember that children will take a lot longer to prepare food than an adult. Time making the dish at home and then double or even treble the time to allow for the children. Do not forget the time needed for hand washing, clearing away at the end and sampling the finished results.

Interest value of the dishes

Often in the nursery the cooking can link with the theme of the week. For example, a colour theme: make biscuits or cakes and ice with food colouring; animals: use animal shapes for sandwiches; and or for an autumn theme: make leaf-shaped biscuits.

The theme could just be for the cooking session, e.g. making jam tarts and singing the 'Queen of Hearts'; telling the time and decorating a cake with a clock face. The cooking could link with a visit to the zoo, park, farm, seaside or to the countryside.

Seasonal themes are easy to use for cooking, e.g.:
• Easter: painted hard-boiled eggs, blancmange rabbits, chocolate nests, bunny and chicken biscuits, hot cross buns.
• Christmas: chocolate log, star- and tree-shaped biscuits, mince pies.
• St Valentine's day: heart-shaped biscuits and cakes.

- Hallowe'en: witch and ghost shapes for sandwiches, biscuits and cakes.
- Bonfire night: baked potatoes, hot dogs.

DURING THE LESSON

A poster or flip-chart of the main stages in the cooking process could be produced. Go through this before the lesson starts.

For older children write captions under each stage in clear writing so that the children can read it.

Hygiene

Before starting to cook always insist on good hygienic practices by making sure that everyone:
- washes their hands;
- ties long hair back;
- puts on aprons;
- wipes the table or covering clean.
- remembers that licking fingers with the mixture is not allowed and that any food dropped should be thrown away.

Cooking

Collect all the ingredients and equipment needed. Weigh out all the ingredients, helping each child read the scales. (*NB* if the children are taught the metric system in maths lessons *do not* confuse them by talking in imperial weights (pounds and ounces)). Any child whose mother does little baking at home will have to be shown how to cream or rub in, etc.

If you are demonstrating a dish, make sure that all the children can see what you are doing, by using a glass mixing bowl and moving other equipment that may block the view. Pass the bowl around so that the children can see and feel the various consistencies of the mixture.

During the cooking you can talk about where the ingredients come from, weighing and measuring, simple nutrition, what the children like to eat and if they cook at home, as well as explaining the various stages of cooking.

Emphasise safety points, e.g. not touching a hot oven, baking tray, care with knives, etc. If the dish is being cooked, it can be timed using a cardboard clock.

After the cooking make sure that all the children are involved with washing up, clearing away and generally tidying up.

AFTER THE LESSON

Make sure enough is made for every child in the class to sample whatever has been made. Present the food carefully and allow the children who have cooked to hand the food around.

VALUE OF COOKING

During cookery sessions the children are able to develop:
• physical and social skills;
• emotionally and intellectually.

Physical skills

Gross motor skills can be developed by beating, kneading, mixing, washing up, etc. Fine motor skills are also developed by cutting out shapes with a cutter in pastry, decorating cakes with cherries or other small decorations. Fresh fruit and vegetables can be prepared by peeling, coring and cutting into small pieces. Hand to eye co-ordination is also developed.

Social skills

Cooking is a shared group activity. Children usually gain from the experience, especially if they have to share, e.g. take turns at beating the mixture, etc.

When the children are sharing what they have made they learn how to present food attractively and to offer it properly.

Emotional development

Children achieve a sense of enjoyment in cookery lessons as well as having the satisfaction of producing an end-product. Children are very proud of what they have cooked. Often the children relate what they have made in school to what they have at home or what their parents or siblings make.

Intellectual development

The scope for intellectual development in cooking is endless. For example, mathematical and scientific concepts such as counting, adding, shapes, weighing, telling the time, the effect of heat on mixtures and the changes in texture of mixtures can all be demonstrated in cookery. Every time a child cooks he is dealing with scientific principles. For example, mixing powdered drinks can introduce words like 'dissolve' and 'solution.' Cocoa powder or stock cubes could be dissolved in hot and cold milk or water to show the effects of heat. When preparing fruit and vegetables children can discover the structure of them, particularly vegetables such as sprouts and cabbage which can be 'unwrapped'. Unusual fruit and vegetables can be taken to the school or nursery for children to try. Simple geography can be introduced by looking at where the ingredients come from. Basic nutrition, kitchen safety and hygiene can all be introduced in cookery lessons.

QUESTIONS

1. Plan the food that you would give for a party with a pirate theme for six 4–5-year-olds.
2. What are the benefits gained from cooking with children in schools?
3. What would you choose to cook for (a) a May-Day theme, (b) a shapes theme in school?

INDEX